BATMAN
THE CAPED CRUSADER
VOLUME 6

BATM
THE CAPED
CRUSADER
VOLUME 6

**ALAN GRANT
DOUG MOENCH
JOHN WAGNER**
writers

**JIM APARO
NORM BREYFOGLE
CAM KENNEDY
TOM MANDRAKE**
artists

ADRIENNE ROY
colorist

**JIM APARO
TODD KLEIN
ALBERT DeGUZMAN
JOHN COSTANZA**
letterers

**NORM BREYFOGLE
and ALLEN PASSALAQUA**
collection cover artists

BATMAN created by
BOB KANE with BILL FINGER

DENNIS O'NEIL Editor – Original Series
KELLEY PUCKETT SCOTT PETERSON Associate Editors – Original Series
REZA LOKMAN Editor – Collected Edition
STEVE COOK Design Director – Books
LOUIS PRANDI Publication Design
ERIN VANOVER Publication Production

MARIE JAVINS Editor-in-Chief, DC Comics

DANIEL CHERRY III Senior VP – General Manager
JIM LEE Publisher & Chief Creative Officer
JOEN CHOE VP – Global Brand & Creative Services
DON FALLETTI VP – Manufacturing Operations & Workflow Management
LAWRENCE GANEM VP – Talent Services
ALISON GILL Senior VP – Manufacturing & Operations
NICK J. NAPOLITANO VP – Manufacturing Administration & Design
NANCY SPEARS VP – Revenue

BATMAN: THE CAPED CRUSADER VOL. 6

DC Comics, 2900 West Alameda Ave., Burbank, CA 91505
Printed by LSC Communications, Owensville, MO, USA. 12/31/21. First Printing.
ISBN: 978-1-77950-800-3

Library of Congress Cataloging-in-Publication Data is available.

PEFC Certified

This product is from
sustainably managed
forests and controlled
sources

PEFC/29-31-337   www.pefc.org

COVER BY
NORM BREYFOGLE

HE'S GACK!
GIGGER--GOLDER--GADDER THAN EVER GEFORE!

The Return of SCARFACE!

PART ONE: MUSTACHE PETE IS DEAD!

ALAN GRANT SCRIPT   NORM BREYFOGLE ART   ADRIENNE ROY COLORS   TODD KLEIN LETTERS   KELLEY PUCKETT ASSOC. EDITOR   DENNIS O'NEIL EDITOR   BOB KANE BATMAN CREATOR

9

I DON'T HAVE TIME FOR JOKES. I'M LATE AS IT IS!

JUST MAKE SURE THESE BOYS ARRIVE AT H.Q. IN *ONE PIECE!*

PAF

ZWEEEEEEEFFT

TRAITOR! YA SOLD US OUT! I--

NOW AIN'T DA TIME, RHINO!

WMP!

KRAK!

DUMMY AIN'T AS *DUMB* AS IT LOOKS, MAN!

ET TU, GRUTE, EH?

I...I DIDN'T HAVE ANY CHOICE, SCARFACE. THEY'D HAVE *KILLED* ME IF I DIDN'T THROW IN WITH 'EM!

HE SAW *SENSE,* VENTRILOQUIST. AN' IF *YOU GOT ANY BRAINS*--

TALK TA *ME!* I'M DA *GOSS* OF THIS OUTFIT! HE'S JUST *HIRED HELP!*

AWRIGHT, BLOCKHEAD! GET THIS--

--THE DAY OF THE *MUSTACHE PETES* IS *OVER!* 'S TIME YOU *THROWBACK* OLD HOOD-LUMS *RETIRED!*

AN' TO HELP YOU *MAKE* THE DECISION--THE *STREET DEMONZ* HAS TAKEN OVER YOUR TURF!

WHAT HAPPENED? WHO DID THIS?

OH... NOBODY. I WAS JUST...

...HAVING A RETIREMENT PARTY.

I HEARD ABOUT YOUR SENTENCE BEING OVER-TURNED. I CAME TO WARN YOU--

I SAID-- I'M RETIRED.

WAKE UP, RHINO!

VENTRILOQUIST! WHAT--?

LATER. COME ON.

BUT--WE CAN'T JUST LEAVE SCARFACE!

IF YOUR BOSS IS TELLING THE TRUTH, YOU WON'T BE NEEDING HIM.

MAYBE NOT. BUT ME AN' SCARFACE GO BACK A LONG WAY. LEAST I CAN DO IS SHOW HIM A LITTLE RESPECT--

--GIVE HIM A DECENT BURIAL!

G.C.P.D.

8

COMMISSIONER
JAMES W.
GORDON

--BRING IN THE STREET DEMONZ FILE, PLEASE?

RIGHT HERE, COMMISSION--

MADRE DE DIOS!

GET DOWN, SIR!

WHAT IN THE NAME--?

MONTOYA--

--NO!

HOPE I DIDN'T STARTLE YOU.

SORRY. DIDN'T REALIZE YOU HAD COMPANY.

MY NEW ASSISTANT-- RENE MONTOYA. RENE--

THIS IS, AHH... THE BATMAN.

DOES HE ALWAYS COME IN THIS WAY?

AHH... NO. HE'S WORKING WITH ME ON A CASE-- THE STREET DEMONZ THING.

I'VE JUST COME FROM THE VENTRILOQUIST CLUB.

9

DID YOU WARN HIM OFF?

DIDN'T HAVE TO. SOMEBODY--PRESUMABLY STREET DEMONZ--BEAT ME TO IT.

THE DUMMY-- SCARFACE--IS SHOT TO PIECES. AND THE VEN- TRILOQUIST CLAIMS HE'S RETIRED.

GOOD! HIS GANG'S SCATTERED--HIS SUPPLIERS HAVE MOVED ON--AND THE DEMONZ HAVE TAKEN HIS TERRITORY.

LAST THING WE NEED IS SCARFACE STARTING A GANG WAR!

WE WERE JUST GOING TO RUN THROUGH THE FILES AGAIN--SEE IF THERE'S SOME CLUE YOU--WE-- MISSED.

CARE TO JOIN US?

HE ALWAYS LEAVE LIKE THAT, TOO, SIR...?

VICKI VALE--I WANT YOU TO MEET HORTEN SPENCE.

The GOTHAMITE Magazine

GOTHAM'S TOP PHOTO JOURNALIST... I'M HONORED, MISS VALE.

THANK YOU. COMING FROM THE BEST REPORTER ON THE EAST COAST, THAT'S PRAISE INDEED.

AND IT'S VICKI.

10

SO..."WHY THE TITANIC TEAM-UP?", YOU'RE WONDERING.

I'LL TELL YOU IN A WORD: DRUGS.

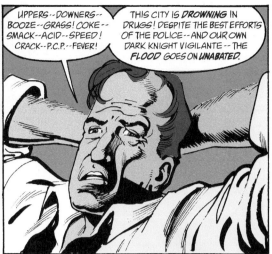

UPPERS--DOWNERS--BOOZE--GRASS! COKE--SMACK--ACID--SPEED! CRACK--P.C.P.--FEVER!

THIS CITY IS *DROWNING* IN DRUGS! DESPITE THE BEST EFFORTS OF THE POLICE--AND OUR OWN DARK KNIGHT VIGILANTE--THE *FLOOD* GOES ON *UNABATED*.

I--AND THOUSANDS OF *OTHER* DECENT CITIZENS--WANT TO KNOW *WHY*. AND *YOU* TWO ARE GOING TO TELL US!

YOU GOT 32 PAGES--EIGHT OF THEM COLOR. DROP ALL OTHER ASSIGNMENTS AS OF *NOW*!

--NOT ASKING FOR MUCH, IS HE? WHERE THE HECK DO WE *BEGIN*?

I'VE A FEW IDEAS. WE CAN--

GOTHAMITE NEWS

IN A MINUTE! I JUST HAVE TO CANCEL BREAKFAST!

Paisano's FINE ITALIAN FOOD

FOOD

BAR

HI, BRUCE, DARLING! SORRY TO KEEP YOU WAITING.

THAT'S ALL RIGHT. I--

THIS IS HORTEN SPENCE, MY NEW PARTNER. HORTEN--*BRUCE WAYNE*.

DELIGHTED, I'M SURE. ER...CARE TO JOIN US, MR. SPENCE...?

11

SORRY, BRUCE -- NOT THIS MORNING. MAJOR ASSIGNMENT -- AND THE METER'S RUNNING!

Paisano's

'O'S FINE ITALIAN FOOD

I'LL CALL YOU!

TO ABSENT FRIENDS!

IT AIN'T RIGHT, VENTRILOQUIST. SCARFACE IS *DEAD*. YA SHOULDN' OUGHTA BE *PARTYIN'*!

HIS DEMISE IS PRECISELY THE REASON, RHINO! NO MORE ORDERING ME AROUND -- NO MORE OF HIS *INSANE* THIRST FOR *VIOLENCE*!

BANG BANG

A HUGE *WEIGHT* HAS BEEN LIFTED FROM MY SHOULDERS! FOR THE FIRST TIME IN YEARS, I FEEL *FREE*! IT'S LIKE... LIKE BEING *BORN AGAIN*!

CHEERS!

GLP!

I'M TELLIN' YA, BOSS -- IT AIN'T RIGHT, SCARFACE WAS A *PART* OF YOU --

I DON'T CARE! THAT'S ALL *OVER*! JUST PUT HIM IN THE *GOX* -- I MEAN THE *BOX*!

SO... SO LONG, SCARFACE! WE HAD SOME TIMES!

12

WHAT WE GONNA DO NOW?

BEATS ME. GO WHERE THE WIND BLOWS US.

...TOMORROW!

I GOT A BROTHER DOIN' WELL IN L.A. MAYBE I'LL LOOK HIM UP...

"LIKE THE ED SAID, DRUGS ARE *EVERY*WHERE, SO WE CAN START *ANY*WHERE!"

"BUT, HORTEN-- A SCHOOL *PLAYGROUND*...?"

"WATCH THE KID IN THE LEATHER VEST--"

13

HUH? DID YOU HEAR THAT, VENTRILOQUIST?

HEAR *WHAT*, OL' BUDDY?

GOYS! I'M HURT GAD! HELP...!

HE'S STILL *ALIVE!*

SHTOOPID! HE WASH *NEVER* ALIVE! HE'S A GLOCKA-- I MEAN, A BLOCKA *WOOD!* LEAVE 'IM *ALONE!*

RHINO, YA GIG LUG! WHAT'RE YA WAITIN' FOR? GET ME OUTA THIS GOX!

R-RIGHT AWAY, BOSS!

TAKE HIM AWAY! I DON'T WANNA SHEE HIM!

YA'LL SEE ME WHETHER YA LIKE IT OR NOT, *GALDY!* YOU NEED *ME* A LOT MORE 'N I NEED *YOU!*

I *DON'T*-- ?HIC?--NEED YOU, SHCARFACE!

OH NO? SO WHADDYA *DONE* SINCE I GOT SHOT? *GOOZE*, DAT'S WHAT!

YOU WAS A DRUNKEN *STUMBLEGUM* GEFORE I MET YA-- AN' YA AIN'T CHANGED ONE *GIT!*

ENOUGHA THE *GULL!* WE GOT PLANS TO MAKE! WE GOT *RATGAGS* TO *GUMP OFF!*

QUIT THIS GALONEY AN' LET'S GET GACK TO GUSINESS!

15

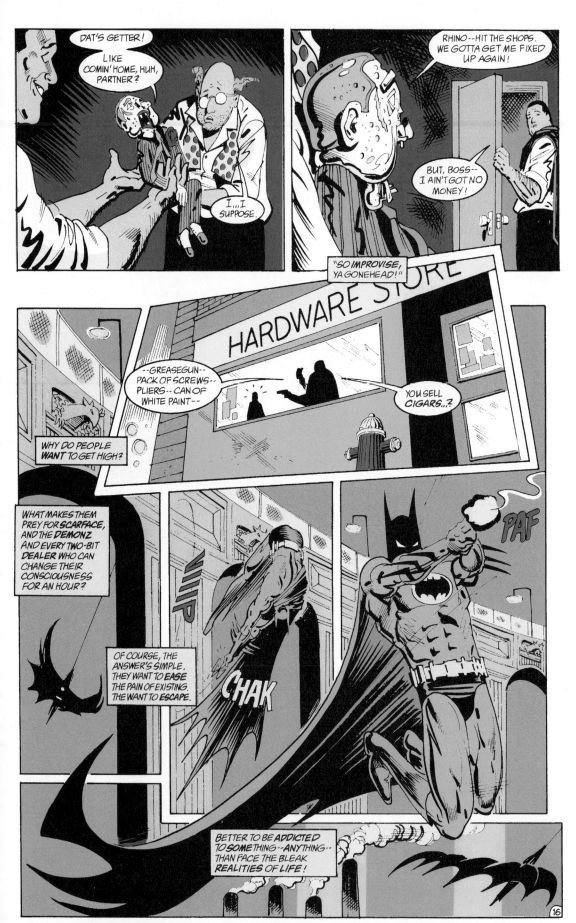

THE NIGHT, AND THE WAR THAT NEVER ENDS.

SCREWDRIVER!

SLAP

SCREWDRIVER!

SQUEE
SQUEE

CHISEL!

SLAP

CHISEL!

TAP TAP

ENOUGH WITH DA ECHO, GEANHEAD!

NUMBER FIVE SANDPAPER!

SLAP

SHIKKKA SHIKKKA SHIKKKA SHIKKKA SHIKKKA

--ONE CUBAN CEEGAR AN' YER GOOD AS NEW, BOSS!

HEY, NOT GAD! NOT GAD AT ALL! A GIT MORE RUGGED LOOKIN'... SCARIER... I LIKE IT!

21

CONTINUED IN DETECTIVE COMICS #642!

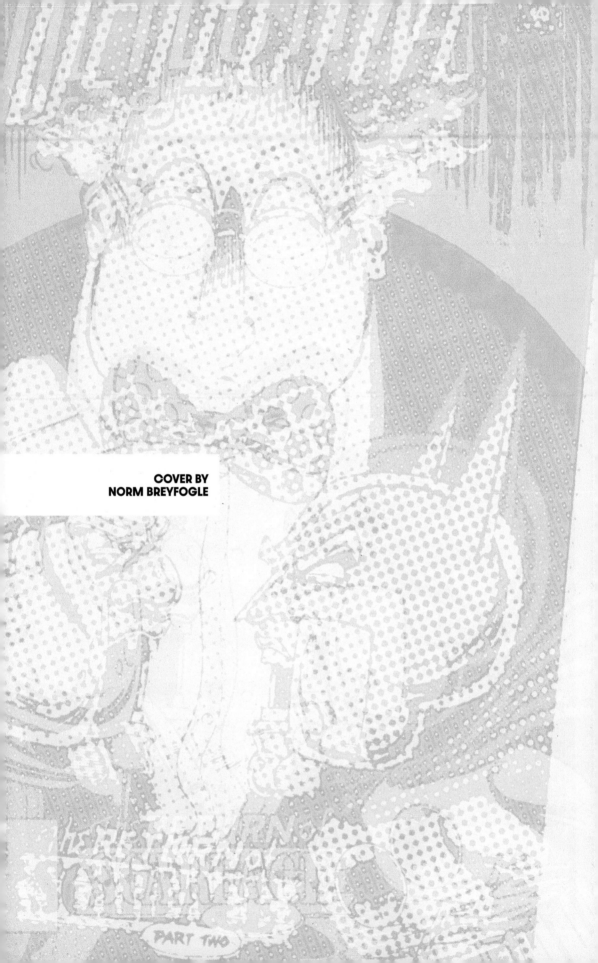

COVER BY
NORM BREYFOGLE

THE RETURN OF SCARFACE

PART 2:

GLEEDING HEARTS

CALL YERSELVES A GANGA GIG-TIME *GAD-GUYS?* LOOK ATCHA!

SO HELP ME, I SEEN *MEANER-* LOOKIN' *GAGIES!*

CONTINUED FROM BATMAN #475

ALAN GRANT	JIM APARO	ADRIENNE ROY	KELLEY PUCKETT	DENNIS O'NEIL	BOB KANE
SCRIPT	ART/LETTERS	COLORIST	ASSISTANT EDITOR	EDITOR	CREATOR

WHAT DA HELL IS *THIS*, GUGSY?

WHUMP

YA STARTED *HIDIN'* YER *LOOT* IN THERE OR SOMETHIN'?

SORRY, *SCARFACE.* I WAS AT THE BEACH WHEN *RHINO* FOUND ME.

WHAAT? I'M IN JAIL – DA *STREET DEMONZ* IS STEALIN' MY TURF – AN' *YOU'RE* AT DA *GEACH*?

AW, GIVE US A BREAK, BOSS. *WE* COULDN'T STOP THE DEMONZ.

THEY AIN'T LIKE US. THEY'RE *CRAZY* – THEY'D *KILL* YA SOON AS LOOK AT YA!

WHY ELSE D'YA THINK I ENDED UP SELLIN' *BURGERS*?

YA OUGHTA END UP *DEAD*, YA USELESS LUMPA GLUGGER!

SLAP

OWW!

AS OF NOW, DIS MOB IS *GACK IN GUSINESS!* IF *DALLAS* AN' HIS GANG THINK THEY CAN WALTZ IN ON *MY* SET-UP, THEY GOT ANOTHER THINK COMIN'--

ALSO A WHOLE LOTTA *FUNERALS!*

2

AW, I DUNNO, SCARFACE. MAYBE DALLAS IS *RIGHT*. THESE DAYS DRUGS *IS* A YOUNG MAN'S GAME.

BESIDES, I KINDA *LIKE* THE *LAWFUL* LIFE. THE MONEY AIN'T GOOD, BUT AT LEAST NOBODY COMES *GUNNIN'* FOR THE BURGER MAN!

IZZATAFACT?

GUDDAGUDDA

AARRGHH!

ANYGODY *ELSE* WANNA *SELL GURGERS*?

N-NOT ME, SCARFACE!

WELCOME BACK, BOSS!

DAT'S GETTER!

YA SHOULD COUNT YERSELVES LUCKY, WORKIN' FER ME. I AIN'T NO GLOCKA WOOD-- I GOT DA *GRAINS* TO *TAKE* US PLACES! NOW LISSEN UP--

GUGSY- GET OUTA DAT EYE-SORE. YOU AN' PETE SEE TA CLEANIN' UP MY *CLUG*. WE'RE OPENIN' AGAIN.

YOU OTHERS - DIG YER *HEATERS* OUTA HOCK AN' GET READY FER *ACTION!*

RHINO, TAKE DA CAR AN' A COUPLE DA GOYS. PICK UP DAT DOITY TRAITOR, *GRUTE*. AN' GE CAREFUL AGOUT IT!

SURE THING, BOSS!

3

GET ME DA *SARGE*, YOU. 'S TIME WE CALLED IN A FEW *FAVORS*.

ARE YOU SURE IT'S *WISE*, SCARFACE? I *THINK*--

YA AIN'T *PAID* TA THINK, *VENTRILOQUIST!* I AIN'T FORGETTIN' HOW YA TRIED TA *RAT* ON ME. NEXT TIME, I GET ME A *NEW* STRAIGHT MAN!

NOW-- DIAL DA *NUMGER!*

-- YOU NEED *WHAT?* BUT THAT'S *INSANE!* I *CAN'T*--

RESTRICTED AREA

MP

MUNITION UNITED STATES GOVERN

CUT DA GULL, *SARGE!* IT'S WORTH *FIFTY THOU* TO YA. THAT HELP CHANGE YER MIND?

JUST SO HAPPENS WE HAVE SOME COMING IN RIGHT NOW-- HOME FROM THE GULF, Y'KNOW.

NOW... HOW ABOUT *AMMO?* GOTTA COST EXTRA.

I GOTTA *WAR* TA *WIN!*

YOU JUST SAID THE MAGIC WORDS.

JUST GIMME WHAT I *NEED!*

4

35

OH, WE'VE HAD GOOD TIMES, I KNOW— BUT EVERYTHING HAS BEEN SO **SUPERFICIAL** BETWEEN US.

I'VE ALWAYS FELT THAT— WELL, YOU NEVER LET ME GET NEAR THE **REAL** YOU, THE ONE YOU **HIDE AWAY** UNDER THAT **PLAYBOY FOP IMAGE.**

PERHAPS THERE **ISN'T** ANY MORE. PERHAPS WHAT YOU **SEE** IS WHAT YOU **GET.**

I'M SORRY, BRUCE. I DIDN'T MEAN TO INSULT YOU.

HE'S SURPRISED BY HIS SUDDEN ANGER, BY THE BITTER WORDS HE HAD NEVER REHEARSED--

DON'T PATRONIZE ME! YOU WOULDN'T TREAT **HORTEN SPENCE** LIKE THAT!

I TAKE IT HE **IS** THE CAUSE OF YOUR SUDDEN CHANGE IN AFFECTIONS?

THAT'S NONE OF YOUR BUSINESS!

LOOK, I THINK ENOUGH'S BEEN SAID. LET'S JUST LEAVE IT HERE.

GOODBYE.

VICKI, I--

GOODBYE, BRUCE!

6

SURE, SONNY. LET'S DO THAT. ONLY—DON'T COUNT ON *WALKING* BACK OUT!

AND THE NAME IS MONTOYA—*SERGEANT* TO YOU!

ULP! I WAS JUST *FOOLIN'*..!

ALL RIGHT— ON YOUR WAY, OR WE'LL RUN YOU IN FOR *LOITERING!*

IN YER EAR, COP!

HAVE A DOG OF A NIGHT!

HAW HAW!

I WONDER WHAT HAPPENED TO RE-SPECT FOR THE *LAW?*

YOU SAW--?

ONE OF THOSE KIDS *BULLOCK* ARRESTED LAST NIGHT TALKED. SAID THE DEMONZ STREET-SELL FROM HERE. BUT THEY WERE CLEAN. HAD TO LET 'EM GO.

BLAST THEM! WE *KNOW* THEY'RE SELLING EVERY KIND OF *DOPE* IN TOWN — AND THEY'RE SO WELL-ORGANIZED, WE CAN'T EVER *TOUCH* THEM!

PERHAPS IF YOU OPENED YOUR *MOUTH* LESS AND YOUR *EYES* MORE, DETECTIVE --

10

CRACK COCAINE!

THEY MUST HAVE SPOTTED US--DUMPED IT BEFORE WE JUMPED THEM!

AND CANVAS WON'T TAKE FINGERPRINTS! BLAST!

BETTER LUCK NEXT TIME!

FWIIP

SHEESH! I WONDER WHAT'S EATING HIM..?

STILL, NICE TO KNOW SOMETHING IS. SHOWS HE'S HUMAN AFTER ALL!

HE'S THAT ALL RIGHT, HARVEY--

MAYBE MORE HUMAN THAN THE REST OF US PUT TOGETHER!

11

LOOKS LIKE THERE'S BEEN AN ACCIDENT!

CALL IT IN, CHUCK. I'LL SEE IF THE DRIVER'S OKAY--

FUNNY. I DON'T SEE--

AAAAGH!

KCHOW
KCHOW
KCHOW
KCHOW

I WOULDN'T BOTHER, CHUCK--

YOU'RE OFF THE AIR!

12

43

SO VICKI VALE IS OUT OF HIS LIFE. GOOD.

A RESPONSIBILITY SHED, LIGHTENING HIS LOAD, EVEN IF ONLY A LITTLE.

IT'S *DRUGS* THAT CONCERN HIM, A *PLAGUE* THAT THREATENS TO *SWAMP* THE CITY HE'S SWORN TO DEFEND AGAINST *ALL* EVIL.

THERE'S AN *ARMY* OF KIDS PEDDLING DEATH ON HIS STREETS. THEY'VE A DOZEN *SAFE HOUSES* THAT THEY ROTATE—A SUPPLIER WHOSE NAME HE'S NEVER HEARD—

WHERE THE HELL DOES HE *START*?

READY?

KLIK

THIS ISN'T QUITE WHAT I HAD IN MIND WHEN I ASKED YOU FOR THAT *DATE--!*

I KNOW, *HORTEN.* BUT LET'S GET THIS *STORY* DONE FIRST.

HE'S THE THIRD IN THE LAST TEN MINUTES. LOOKS LIKE WE STRUCK *LUCKY!*

SHOULDN'T WE TELL THE POLICE?

FOR ALL THE GOOD IT'LL DO. THE GANGS FORTIFY THEM WITH *STEEL PLATE.* BY THE TIME THE POLICE BREAK IN, THE *DRUGS* ARE FLUSHING ALONG SOME *SEWER* AND *ANOTHER* SAFE-HOUSE IS OPENING UP!

NO, THEY HAVE TO COME OUT SOMETIME. IF WE WAIT, YOU CAN PHOTOGRAPH THEM. WE MIGHT GET A LEAD TO THE *NEXT* RUNG IN THEIR HIERARCHY--

RRUMMBBLLEE

WHAT IN THE NAME--?

16

BUSINESS IS SLACK TONIGHT.

YEAH. MUST BE SOMETHIN' GOOD ON TV--!

'S OKAY. *DALLAS* SAID HE WANTED TO *COOL* THINGS *OFF* A LITTLE TILL HE SETS UP OUR NEXT SHIPMENT.

demonz rule ya geek

WHERE IS HE, ANYWAY?

WHO KNOWS, WITH DALLAS?

WHAT'S THAT NOISE?

CHECK IT, *JAZZY!*

HOLY TOAST AN' CREAM CHEESES! *GETALOADATHAT!*

IN POSITION NOW, CHIEF! WHAT ORDERS?

GLOW DA LOW-LIFES TA HELL AN' GACK!

17

48

--LEAST *ELEVEN* PEOPLE *DIED* IN THE ATTACK, WITH THE LIKELIHOOD OF *MORE* STILL BURIED IN THE RUBBLE!

MEANWHILE, TWO BODIES HAVE BEEN DISCOVERED NEAR THE DOCKS, BELIEVED TO BE THE *CREW* OF THE STOLEN TRANSPORTER.

TWO WELL-KNOWN GOTHAM JOURNALISTS - *VICKI VALE* AND *HORTEN SPENCE* - WERE WOUNDED IN THE *CROSSFIRE*.

POLICE SUSPECT A FIRE AND ATTACK ON SHOPS IN THE *LAMONT DISTRICT* WERE A *DIVERSIONARY* TACTIC, DRAWING OFFICERS AWAY FROM THE REAL CRIME.

COMMISSIONER JAMES *GORDON* HAD THIS TO SAY--

"MAKE NO MISTAKE - THIS CITY WILL *NOT* TOLERATE VIOLENCE ON THIS SCALE! WE *WILL* FIND THE CULP--

KLICK

SIR!

MISS VICKI--? I JUST HEARD...

SHE'S IN INTENSIVE CARE. SPENCE, TOO. THEY'RE LUCKY TO BE ALIVE.

21

COFFEE? I'M SURE YOU COULD USE--

NO. I'LL BE IN THE STUDY. DON'T DISTURB ME.

SHE COULD HAVE BEEN KILLED. SHE'D HAVE DIED NEVER HAVING KNOWN THAT HE *LOVED* HER-- NEVER KNOWING ANYTHING AT ALL ABOUT HIM...

THE *REAL* HIM--NOT SOME FOP HE'S INVENTED TO KEEP THE WORLD OUT OF HIS HAIR!

AND SUDDENLY, HE *KNOWS* WHAT HE'S GOING TO DO.

PART 3 - *THE GIG HEAT* - IS IN BATMAN #476!

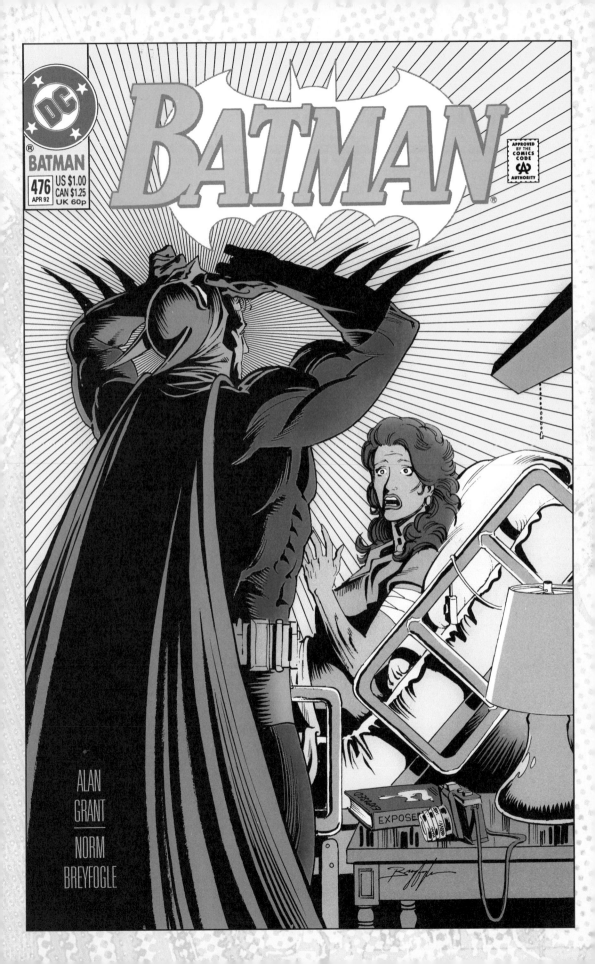

COVER BY
NORM BREYFOGLE

57

LAME QUESTION-- HOW DO YOU FEEL?

ABOUT TWICE AS BAD AS I LOOK! I SUPPOSE I'M LUCKY TO BE ALIVE.

POOR *HORTEN* GOT IT WORSE. FOUR BULLETS IN HIS LEGS...!

I'M SORRY FOR HIM. DID YOU SEE WHO--?

NO. IT WAS DARK--THEIR HEAD-LIGHTS WERE IN OUR EYES. MY CAMERA, FILM, ALL OUR EVIDENCE-- WAS DESTROYED.

I'M SURE THE POLICE WILL FIND THEM.

BUT THAT ISN'T WHY I CAME, VICKI. IT MAY NOT BE THE RIGHT TIME OR PLACE FOR IT--BUT I HAVE ...SOMETHING *IMPORTANT* TO SAY.

HIS MOUTH IS SUDDENLY DRY. HIS TONGUE FEELS FAT AND SWOLLEN. THIS IS A SECRET HE THOUGHT HE'D *NEVER* SHARE. IT ISN'T COMING EASY.

WELL? WHAT...?

BUT HE *LOVES* HER. HE WANTS HER BACK. AND *THIS* IS THE ONLY WAY HE MIGHT GET HER--

VICKI, I WANT YOU TO KNOW THAT I'M NOT...WHAT I SEEM.

I...I'M--

SERGEANT ESSEN...?

JIM HAD AN ANONYMOUS PHONE CALL, TOLD US WHERE THE STREET DEMONZ' BIG DEAL IS GOING DOWN.

HE WENT ON WITH THE SQUAD. HE ASKED ME TO WAIT FOR YOU.

ANONYMOUS... IT COULD BE ANOTHER DIVERSION, LIKE LAST NIGHT'S ARSON ATTACK. IT'D TAKE THE HEAT OFF THE REAL MEET.

OR IT COULD BE A TRAP!

WE CONSIDERED THAT. THE CALLER SAID ONLY YOU WOULD BE ABLE TO GET INSIDE. BUT JIM HAD TO GO.

THEY'RE AT THE OLD CHEM-PLANT ON HUDSON.

CLEAR ACROSS TOWN -- AND I DON'T HAVE THE BATMOBILE!

THE BATMAN NEEDS A CHAUFFEUR? COME ON!

STAIRS

VRRMM

VRRRRR

COMMISSIONER? TWO VEHICLES--HEADING FOR THE PLANT!

LOOKS LIKE OUR MAN WASN'T LYING! MAINTAIN YOUR POSITION, BULLOCK. WAIT FOR MY SIGNAL.

8

YOU SPOTTED THOSE GUARDS YET?

YES, SIR. AT LEAST TWO OF THEM.

POLICE

DOESN'T LOOK LIKE BATMAN'S GOING TO SHOW. WELL, WE CAN'T AFFORD TO WAIT.

MONTOYA-- SHOW THEM WHERE THE GUARDS ARE. I WANT THEM TAKEN AS QUIETLY AS POSSIBLE.

THEN PASS THE WORD-- WE'RE MOVING IN!

THE NAME'S SCARFACE, DOLL. I BELIEVE I GOT A RESERVATION...?

IF YOU'D WALK THIS WAY, GENTLEMEN.

SURE THING, BABE!

HAW HAW!

SLAP!

CUT IT OUT, YA GIG GALOOT! AIN'T YA GOT NO CLASS?

9

DON'T GO IN THERE, SERGEANT. BATMAN SAYS THE PLACE IS GOING TO *EXPLODE!*

COMMISSIONER GORDON-- WHERE IS HE?

HE WAS FIRST IN-- CHASED 'EM UP THE WALKWAY. I HAVEN'T SEEN HIM SINCE!

JIM! JIM!

NOT A GOOD IDEA, SERGEANT!

LET ME GO, I HAVE TO GET JIM--!

TAKE HER OUT--

--AND MAKE SURE SHE DOESN'T COME BACK *IN!*

PAF

NO! I CAN'T LEAVE HIM. PLEASE--!

I'LL FIND THE COMMISSIONER!

CLMP

ZZWEEEEEEEEE

THE COPS ARE RUNNIN', DALLAS!

THAT JUST LEAVES THE BAT- CREEP! *DROP* HIM!

POW

BADAD

SPANG

CHING

SPAK

VREEOW

WHERE ARE YOU, JIM...?

15

MAYBE WE *DID* GET BATMAN AN' THE DEMONZ--BUT WE DIDN'T GET THE *MONEY*--OR THE *DOPE!*

CHUMP! DIS AIN'T AGOUT MONEY! I GOT CASH STASHED ALL OVER DA CITY!

IT'S AGOUT *POWER.* IT'S AGOUT WHO *GIVES* DA ORDERS--AN' WHO *OGEYS* 'EM!

IT'S AGOUT *FEAR*--AGOUT LETTIN' EVERY-GODY AN' HIS MONKEY KNOW WHO'S *GOSS!*

AIN'T DAT A FACT NOW, *GRUTE?*

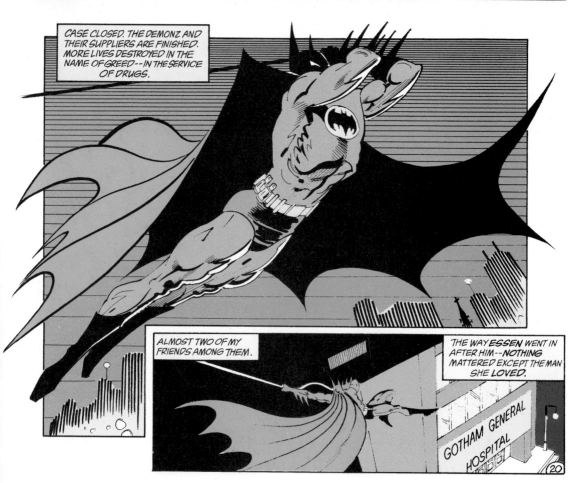

CASE CLOSED. THE DEMONZ AND THEIR SUPPLIERS ARE FINISHED. MORE LIVES DESTROYED IN THE NAME OF GREED--IN THE SERVICE OF DRUGS.

ALMOST TWO OF MY FRIENDS AMONG THEM.

THE WAY *ESSEN* WENT IN AFTER HIM--*NOTHING* MATTERED EXCEPT THE MAN SHE *LOVED.*

GOTHAM GENERAL HOSPITAL

20

AND HER LOVE MIGHT HAVE *KILLED* THE *BOTH* OF THEM!

MISS VALE? I KNOW IT'S LATE-- BUT YOUR VISITOR'S BACK. DO YOU WANT TO SEE HIM?

I CAN'T SLEEP. YES-- SEND HIM IN.

SORRY I HAD TO RUSH OFF LIKE THAT--I COMPLETELY FORGOT ABOUT THAT *BUSINESS SUPPER!*

JUST LIKE YOU, BRUCE!

YOU WERE GOING TO TELL ME SOMETHING...?

I WAS? OH! YES, OF COURSE.

I JUST WANT YOU TO KNOW, VICKI...

EVEN IF WE'RE NOT GOING OUT TOGETHER, YOU'RE VERY IMPORTANT TO ME.

TAKE BETTER CARE OF YOURSELF. *PLEASE...!*

AND I THOUGHT IT WAS SOMETHING *WORLD-SHATTERING!*

OH, BRUCE-- YOU'RE SO SWEET...!

WELL, OLD GUDDY--I GUESS THIS IS WHERE WE PART COMPANY...!

21

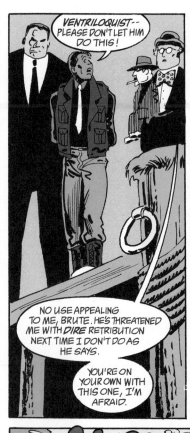

The End

BATMAN

477
EARLY
MAY 92

US $1.25
CAN $1.50
UK 60p

APPROVED
BY THE
COMICS
CODE
AUTHORITY

Gotham

PART ONE ▲ BY WAGNER & KENNEDY

COVER BY
TOM TAGGART

When clouds o'ershadow
   night's great eye,
And winged creatures swirl
   on dark'ning sky;
When north wind's chill
   breath winds
Through Gotham's caverns,
   caressing every spine.
In that hour the Gargoyle
   stalks his prey,
And darker demons speed
   the dawn of judgment day...

A GOTHAM TALE PART I GARGOYLES

JOHN WAGNER - WRITER * CAM KENNEDY - ARTIST * ALBERT DEGUZMAN - LETTERER
ADRIENNE ROY - COLORIST * KELLEY PUCKETT - ASST. EDITOR * DENNY O'NEIL - EDITOR
BATMAN created by BOB KANE

HE DOESN'T HAVE TO SEARCH TONIGHT--

--DOESN'T HAVE TO COURSE THE CITY STREETS, LISTENING FOR THE SCREAM, WATCHING FOR THE FLASH OF STEEL OR THE GLINT OF EVIL IN A MAN'S EYES...

TONIGHT HE KNOWS.

TIME AND PLACE.

THE TREASURES OF CANTERBURY

EXHIBITION OPEN TODAY

GOOD THING, TOO.

LOOKS LIKE RAIN.

2

CHOP CHOP, BOYS! WE'VE ALL GOT HOMES TO GO TO!

DO BE CAREFUL, DEREK! THAT IS NOT A *FRISBEE* YOU'RE CARRYING, PLEASE!

WHERE DID YOU SAY YOU WORKED BEFORE—U.S. STEEL?

THE SHRINE OF ST. THOMAS BECKET...

FOR OVER THREE HUNDRED YEARS *PILGRIMS* FLOCKED TO IT FROM EVERY PART OF ENGLAND.

THE WOODEN COVER PROTECTED THE SAINT'S BONES. WHEN IT WAS RAISED, SILVER BELLS WERE RUNG TO CALL THE PILGRIMS.

THIS IS A RECONSTRUCTION, OF COURSE. THE ORIGINAL SHRINE WAS DESTROYED IN 1538.

THE SECTION OF THOMAS'S SKULL CHOPPED OFF BY HIS MURDERERS WAS HELD SEPARATELY, IN THE CORONA. BUT THAT WAS LOST, TOO.

③

"FASCINATING, MY DEAR! MOST FASCINATING!"

"SO MUCH HISTORY! THE TREASURES OF MEDIEVAL ENGLAND! TO HAVE THEM HERE IN GOTHAM, UNDER ONE ROOF-- IT'S A MARVELOUS ACHIEVEMENT!"

"I THOUGHT YOU'D APPRECIATE A PRIVATE VIEWING, AFTER THE CROWDS HAD GONE."

"I DO INDEED! YOU'RE MOST KIND TO REMEMBER ME, AFTER ALL THESE YEARS."

"AH, CHAUCER'S PILGRIMS EN ROUTE TO CANTERBURY..."

"WHATEVER ELSE YOU MAY THINK OF HIM, CHRISTINA, YOUR FATHER'S TRANSLATION OF THE CANTERBURY TALES WILL REMAIN ONE OF THE CLASSICS OF THE ENGLISH LANGUAGE."

"YOU'LL FORGIVE ME IF I FIND IT HARD TO TAKE COMFORT FROM THAT AT THE MOMENT."

"ARE WE GOING TO BE MUCH LONGER, MISS CREIGHTON? HMMM?"

"JUST A FEW MINUTES, MICHAEL."

"IT'S A CONDITION OF OUR ARRANGEMENT WITH THE CANTERBURY CATHEDRAL THAT THE MORE PORTABLE OBJECTS BE LOCKED IN THE GALLERY VAULT WHILE NOT ACTUALLY ON EXHIBITION."

"QUITE RIGHT. CAN'T BE TOO SAFE."

"WITH CARE, RODNEY! WITH CARE!"

"THEY'VE MANAGED TO PRESERVE THAT SAINTED HAND FOR EIGHT HUNDRED YEARS-- WE ONLY HAVE IT A WEEK."

"THE LEAST WE CAN DO IS RETURN IT DIGITUS INTACTUS."

4

"I MUST SAY, YOU SHOW REMARKABLE FORTITUDE, CARRYING ON WITH THE EXHIBITION AFTER ALL THAT HAS HAPPENED..."

MY FATHER DIED THREE WEEKS AGO · THIS EXHIBITION HAS BEEN PLANNED FOR OVER A YEAR. I CAN'T LET PERSONAL GRIEF INTERFERE WITH MY DUTY.

BESIDES, THE PROCEEDS GO TO A VERY GOOD CAUSE.

YOUR ATTITUDE DOES YOU CREDIT. YOU'VE GROWN INTO A FINE YOUNG WOMAN, MY DEAR.

⑤

LITTLE CHRISTINA! TO THINK ALL THOSE YEARS AGO I BOUNCED YOU ON MY KNEE! IT WAS A SOURCE OF....GREAT REGRET TO ME WHEN YOUR FATHER CHOSE TO SEND YOU AWAY.

NOW YOU KNOW WHY....

TO PROTECT ME....FROM HIMSELF.

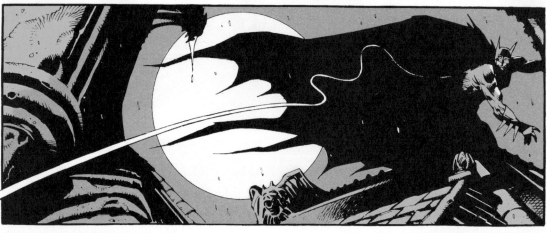

YOU WERE HIS FRIEND. YOU WORKED WITH HIM. IN ALL THOSE YEARS DID YOU NEVER SUSPECT WHAT KIND OF....MONSTER HE'D BECOME?

NO....

AS I SAID AT THE INQUEST, MY PART IN HIS EXPERIMENTS WAS MERCIFULLY BRIEF. I THOUGHT THE WHOLE FOOLISH VENTURE FORGOTTEN. I NEVER ONCE CONNECTED DAVID WITH THE GARGOYLE....

DON'T BE TOO HARSH ON HIM, MY DEAR. HE COULDN'T HELP HIM-SELF. IT'S HARD FOR YOU TO UNDERSTAND, BUT.... THE THING WAS STRONGER THAN HE WAS.

BRRINGG

6

THIS IS NOT A SHOOTING GALLERY! I'LL THANK YOU GENTLEMEN TO LEAVE THE PREMISES!

I'LL THANK YOU TO DROP DEAD!

85

"I HEARD A MECHANISM ENGAGE..."

THIS DOOR—IT'S ON A *TIME LOCK* ?

YES... IT OPENS AT SEVEN-THIRTY IN THE MORNING, TO GIVE THEM TIME TO PUT THE EXHIBITS ON DISPLAY.

I... I SUPPOSE WE'RE STUCK IN HERE TILL THEN.

THOSE POOR SOULS... THEY WON'T BE DOING ANYTHING IN THE MORNING...

AT LEAST WE'RE SAFE IN HERE, BE THANKFUL FOR THAT.

THOSE IDIOTS—DO YOU SEE WHAT THEY'VE DONE ? ANYTHING THEY MIGHT HAVE BEEN ABLE TO CARRY AWAY IS IN HERE. THEY'VE EFFECTIVELY LOCKED UP WHAT THEY CAME TO STEAL !

QUITE AN IRONY !

NOT MANY CRIMINALS JOIN MENSA, DOCTOR.

YOU ARE DOCTOR MORRIS EAGLETON, AREN'T YOU—SENIOR BIOCHEMIST AT THE GOTHAM INSTITUTE ?

HOW DID YOU KNOW ?

YOU WERE THE PRINCIPAL WITNESS AT THE INQUEST ON DAVID CREIGHTON, ALIAS THE *GARGOYLE.* YOUR PICTURE WAS PLASTERED ALL OVER THE PAPERS.

AS YOU MAY KNOW, I TOOK A CERTAIN INTEREST IN THE GARGOYLE, TOO.

11

AND YOU, MISS- YOU MUST BE CREIGHTON'S DAUGHTER, CHRISTINA. YOU CAME OVER FROM ENGLAND FOR THE INQUEST.

I WAS DUE TO COME IN ANY CASE FOR THIS EXHIBITION. MY FATHER'S DEATH WAS AN UNFORTUNATE... COINCIDENCE.

AND NOW... NOW THREE MORE INNOCENT MEN HAVE BEEN MURDERED...

IT MIGHT NOT STOP AT THREE. THIS VAULT IS AIRTIGHT, ISN'T IT?

I...I BELIEVE SO. THEY GENERALLY STORE PAINTINGS HERE. IT HELPS TO PRESERVE THEM.

WHAT'S WRONG-?

IT'S JUST AFTER TEN NOW. THE VAULT DOESN'T OPEN UNTIL SEVEN-THIRTY TOMORROW MORNING- THAT'S MORE THAN NINE HOURS.

AT A ROUGH CALCULATION I'D SAY WE'VE GOT FIVE THOUSAND CUBIC FEET OF AIR IN HERE.

YOU'RE THE BIOCHEMIST. YOU SHOULD BE ABLE TO WORK IT OUT FOR YOURSELF.

THREE OF US... ALLOWING FOR FACTORS OF STRESS, LEVEL OF ACTIVITY ET CETERA...

MY GOD! ABOUT THREE AND A HALF HOURS!

SAY FOUR HOURS MAX BEFORE THE AIR RUNS OUT.

B-BUT SURELY HELP WILL COME...!

THAT DOOR'S A DODDS STRUTTON TWE'VE SERIES. THE SAME THING HAPPENED TO A BANK EMPLOYEE IN ARKANSAS. IT TOOK FIVE HOURS JUST TO BURN AN AIRHOLE THROUGH.

BY THAT TIME THE BANK EMPLOYEE HAD CASHED IN, AS THEY SAY.

FIVE HOURS. WE'VE GOT FOUR.

THEN... THEN WE'RE ALL GOING TO DIE...

THERE IS ANOTHER SOLUTION. NOT A VERY PLEASANT ONE, I'M AFRAID.

THREE OF US WON'T MAKE IT.

BUT TWO OF US MIGHT.

12

KEEP BACK NOW, FOLKS.

WHAT'S GOING ON?

THERE'S BEEN A ROBBERY—SOME PEOPLE TRAPPED IN THE VAULT.

MOVE ALONG NOW. THERE'S NOTHING TO DO HERE BUT GET WET.

DEE DEE DEE DIT DIT DIT

DEE DEE DIT DEE DIT DIT

THEY'RE SENDING FOR CUTTING EQUIPMENT. ESTIMATE TWENTY MINUTES.

13

THAT'S FIVE AND A HALF HOURS BEFORE THEY CAN BE THROUGH.

TRANQUILIZER DARTS.

ONE PUTS YOU OUT-THREE MAKES IT PERMANENT.

TIME'S RUNNING OUT. LEAVE IT MUCH LONGER AND THERE'LL ONLY BE ENOUGH AIR FOR ONE. WE HAVE TO DECIDE NOW.

THIS IS INCREDIBLE! I CAN'T TAKE PART IN SUCH A THING!

IT'S A TERRIBLE PROSPECT, MY DEAR, BUT... WHAT BATMAN SAYS MAKES SENSE.

WE MUST BE REALISTIC. IT'S ONE... OR ALL.

AND HOW DO WE CHOOSE WHO DIES? NAMES IN A HAT? DRAW STRAWS? EENY MEENY MINEY MO? YOU CAN'T DECIDE SOMEONE'S LIFE LIKE THAT!

THE CANTERBURY TALES... THAT WAS ALL OVER A DINNER, WASN'T IT?

WHICHEVER PILGRIM TOLD THE BEST TALE WOULD BE BOUGHT A DINNER PAID FOR BY ALL...

14

IT SEEMS APPROPRIATE - THOUGH OUR STAKES ARE MUCH HIGHER.

LET'S LEAVE MISS CREIGHTON OUT OF THIS, DOCTOR. THE TWO OF US WILL TELL OUR TALES - WHY WE SHOULD BE THE ONE TO LIVE. FIVE MINUTES EACH. WE HAVE THAT MUCH TIME.

WHEN WE'VE MADE OUR CASE, ALL THREE DECIDE.

BUT YOU'RE CAPABLE OF KILLING EITHER OF US. IF YOU'RE CHOSEN TO DIE, HOW DO I KNOW YOU'LL GO ALONG WITH IT?

YOU HAVE MY WORD. I DON'T BREAK IT.

VERY WELL. I ACCEPT THAT.

SO DO I.

MISS CREIGHTON-

DON'T COME ANY NEARER! MY MIND'S MADE UP!

SINCE WE'RE ALL AGREED ON THIS DESPERATE COURSE OF ACTION, I WON'T ALLOW YOU TO LEAVE ME OUT. YOU CAN HEAR MY STORY FIRST.

BUT MY DEAR CHRISTINA -

I DON'T WANT ANY FAVORS, DOCTOR. SIT AND LISTEN. PERHAPS I CAN SAVE YOU A LITTLE AIR.

I...SUPPOSE I SHOULD START WHERE IT BEGINS... I WAS TEN. I WAS LIVING WITH MY FATHER AT THE INSTITUTE. MY MOTHER HAD DIED THE YEAR BEFORE. FOR HER SAKE, I'M GRATEFUL.

YOU'LL EXCUSE ME, MISS CREIGHTON, BUT WE DON'T HAVE TIME FOR YOUR LIFE STORY.

THIS WON'T TAKE LONG. PLEASE DO ME THE KINDNESS OF LISTENING.

15

"I WAS NEVER HAPPY AT THE INSTITUTE. AS YOU KNOW, IT'S ONE OF THE FINEST GOTHIC BUILDINGS IN GOTHAM— BUT TO A TEN-YEAR-OLD CHILD IT WAS A PLACE OF TERROR..."

"EACH DARK RECESS HELD SOME IMAGINED HORROR, WAITING TO POUNCE... EACH CARVED GARGOYLE FACE SEEMED FILLED WITH EVIL INTENT, SPECIALLY FOR ME."

"WHEREVER I WENT THEIR EYES WOULD FOLLOW ME..."

"STONE FACES, COLD EYES... BUT I WAS SURE THAT THEY WERE ALIVE, THAT THEY WANTED TO HURT ME..."

"AND ONE NIGHT IT CAME TRUE..."

IS... IS SOMEBODY THERE...?

16

UHH,,,
UHHH,,,
UHHH

DADDEEEEE!

HE WASN'T THERE.
I THOUGHT HE MIGHT
BE WITH YOU, DOCTOR.
YOU OFTEN WORKED
TOGETHER THEN.

YES,,, HE'D
ASKED MY HELP
WITH SOME FORMULAE
HE'D DISCOVERED IN
AN OLD MANUSCRIPT-
JORIX, THE THIRTEENTH
CENTURY ALCHEMIST...

ALCHEMY! IF ONLY I'D
KNOWN WHAT WOULD COME
OF IT!

17

DO NOT BE AFRAID, DEAR ONE... IT WILL SOON BE ALL OVER...

CRASSHHHH!

I'LL BE BACK. YOU'RE SAFE NOW, DON'T CRY.

YOU DIDN'T KNOW WE'D MET BEFORE, DID YOU?

YOU WERE THAT LITTLE GIRL?

THAT WAS THE FIRST TIME I ENCOUNTERED THE GARGOYLE. I GAVE CHASE BUT... IT WAS DARK. I LOST IT.

WHEN I RETURNED YOU WERE GONE.

"THE POLICE FOUND ME WANDERING IN THE STREET. I COULDN'T SPEAK. I WAS TOO TERRIFIED TO TELL THEM WHAT HAD HAPPENED. IT WAS TWO HOURS BEFORE MY FATHER COULD BE LOCATED."

A-A GARGOYLE CAME TO LIFE, DADDY! IT... IT...IT...

THERE THERE, DARLING. EVERYTHING'S ALL RIGHT.

POOR LITTLE SOUL. OVERACTIVE IMAGINATION. IT'S BEEN ROUGH FOR HER SINCE HER MOM DIED.

I'LL TAKE HER HOME.

I USED HER BLOOD, MORRIS!

FOOL THAT I WAS! JUST A FEW DROPS— THAT TIME SHE CUT HERSELF. THAT'S ALL.

I DIDN'T THINK IT WOULD MATTER... BUT...

I WANTED MORE, MORRIS! HER BLOOD—ALL OF IT! IF...IF BATMAN HADN'T STOPPED ME I'D HAVE KILLED HER!

DADDY... I CAN'T SLEEP...

"YOU DIDN'T THINK I REMEMBERED, DID YOU, DOCTOR?"

"YOU SAID AT THE INQUEST THAT YOU NEVER CONNECTED MY FATHER WITH THE GARGOYLE. YOU'VE SAID THE SAME TO ME TONIGHT. BUT YOU KNEW. I HEARD HIM TELL YOU."

"WHY DID YOU LIE, DOCTOR?"

WHAT... WHAT COULD I SAY? THAT I KNEW AND KEPT QUIET ALL THAT TIME BECAUSE... BECAUSE DAVID WAS MY FRIEND. MISGUIDED AS IT MAY HAVE BEEN, I—I WANTED TO PROTECT HIM.

ONCE DAVID WAS DEAD—AND WITH HIM THE GARGOYLE—I... I SAW NO REASON TO IMPLICATE MYSELF...

I SEE.

21

A FEW WEEKS AFTER THAT NIGHT MY FATHER TOLD ME HE WAS SENDING ME AWAY. HE COULDN'T EXPLAIN, BUT IT WOULD BE SAFER IF I WENT AWAY FOR A WHILE.

I WAS TO GO TO A BOARDING SCHOOL IN ENGLAND. ARRANGEMENTS HAD BEEN MADE. I WOULD LEAVE IMMEDIATELY.

"WHEN THE KILLINGS STARTED THE ENGLISH PAPERS SOON PICKED UP ON THEM. BUT NO ONE FOLLOWED THEM WITH QUITE THE COLD, NUMB HORROR THAT I FELT."

"I'D PRAY FOR HIM, PRAY FOR HIS SOUL, PRAY THAT WHAT I'D HEARD THAT NIGHT HAD JUST BEEN A DREAM. BUT I KNEW TOO, DOCTOR..."

GOTHAM GARGOYLE SLAYS No 4

I FELT EACH ONE OF THOSE DEATHS AS IF IT HAD BEEN *ME* WHO KILLED THEM. BECAUSE I KNEW. I COULD HAVE TOLD SOMEONE, I COULD HAVE STOPPED IT. BUT... JUST LIKE YOU I DID NOTHING...

SO MUCH BLOOD ON MY HANDS...

THAT'S WHY I CAN NEVER ASK ANYONE TO DIE FOR ME.

MISS CREIGHTON! NO!

TO BE CONTINUED?

BATMAN

478
LATE
MAY 92
US $1.25
CAN $1.50
UK 60p

APPROVED
BY THE
COMICS CODE
AUTHORITY

PART TWO ▲ BY WAGNER & KENNEDY

**COVER BY
TOM TAGGART**

In that hour the Gargoyle stalks his prey, and spirit, venging spirit speed the knell of Judgment Day ...

A GOTHAM TALE

PART: 2 VENGING SPIRITS

JOHN WAGNER - WRITER * CAM KENNEDY - ARTIST * ALBERT DE GUZMAN - LETTERER
ADRIENNE ROY - COLORIST * KELLEY PUCKETT - ASST. EDITOR * DENNY O'NEIL - EDITOR
BATMAN created by BOB KANE

ONE OF THESE DARTS WOULD GIVE YOU A PLEASANT FORTY WINKS. *THREE* WOULD MOST CERTAINLY BE LETHAL.

YOU'VE NO RIGHT-!

YOU SAID IT YOURSELF-THERE ISN'T ENOUGH AIR FOR THREE! ONE OF US *HAS* TO DIE!

NOT YOU. CALL IT AN OLD-FASHIONED ATTITUDE, MISS CREIGHTON, BUT YOU'RE NOT PART OF THIS DEAL.

WE'RE AGREED ON THAT, AREN'T WE, DOCTOR?

YES....OF COURSE.

THEN IT'S YOU OR ME.

--*DOCTOR MORRIS EAGLETON*, SENIOR BIOCHEMIST AT THE GOTHAM INSTITUTE, *CHRISTINA CREIGHTON*, WHO'S SUPERVISING THE EXHIBITION HERE ..., AND *BATMAN*.

CREIGHTON-ISN'T THAT THE *GARGOYLE'S* DAUGHTER?

HOW DO *THOSE* THREE END UP LOCKED IN A VAULT? WHAT'S BEEN GOING ON HERE?

IS THAT *BLOOD* THEY'RE MOPPIN' UP?

NAH, KETCHUP.

GIMME A BREAK,...!

YOU'LL GET A FULL STATEMENT IN DUE COURSE. RIGHT NOW, ALL I'M CONCERNED ABOUT IS THOSE PEOPLE IN THERE.

HERE AM I, AN OLD MAN... OLDER THAN MY YEARS, PERHAPS, BUT STILL, I'VE HAD MY FAIR CRACK AT LIFE. WHAT HAVE I ACHIEVED? NOTHING OF GREAT NOTE.

IN THE MATTER OF YOUR FATHER, CHRISTINA - IN CONCEALING THE TRUTH ABOUT HIM - AS FAR AS YOU ARE AWARE, I AM AS GUILTY AS YOU.

THEN THERE IS BATMAN.

HERO OF GOTHAM. DARK KNIGHT OF JUSTICE. HOW MANY LIVES HAS HE SAVED? HOW MANY EVILDOERS HAS HE PLACED BEHIND BARS?

AND HE'S YOUNG, STRONG. SO MANY GOOD YEARS AHEAD - FIGHTING CRIME, DEFENDING THE WEAK AND THE INNOCENT...

TELL ME HONESTLY, MY DEAR, WHO CAN YOU CHOOSE TO LIVE BUT HIM?

I CAN'T DECIDE-!

YOU MUST, CHRISTINA. YOU HAVE THE DECIDING VOTE. A TERRIBLE BURDEN ON YOUR YOUNG SHOULDERS, I KNOW...

NEVER MIND. LET ME RELIEVE YOU OF IT. I HAD NO INTENTION OF KEEPING THIS FOOLISH BARGAIN IN ANY CASE.

OH, IF BATMAN HAD BEEN THE ONE CHOSEN FOR CHRISTINA, IT WOULD HAVE SUITED ME WELL ENOUGH — FOR, CHRISTINA, I COULD NOT HAVE LET YOU DIE EITHER... UNLESS IT WAS BY MY OWN HAND.

WH-WHAT ARE YOU TALKING ABOUT?

I DON'T LIKE THE TURN OF THIS CONVERSATION, EAGLETON.

AIR'S RUNNING OUT - GET ON WITH IT.

DON'T WORRY ABOUT AIR. BEFORE LONG, I'M AFRAID, NEITHER OF YOU WILL NEED TO BREATHE.

DEAR, DEAR CHRISTINA... YOU'VE CONVINCED YOURSELF THE REASON DAVID HID YOU AWAY IN ENGLAND WAS TO PROTECT YOU FROM HIMSELF. BUT YOU'RE WRONG. QUITE, QUITE WRONG.

WH- WHAT ARE YOU SAYING? I HEARD MY FATHER CONFESS!

YOU SEE, I AM THE GARGOYLE.

OH, YES, IT'S TRUE - HE WAS THE GARGOYLE THAT FIRST NIGHT. HE DID PURSUE YOU WITH MURDEROUS INTENT. BUT NEVER AGAIN...

I WOULD HAVE KILLED HER, MORRIS! JUST BECAUSE WE USED HER BLOOD IN THE FORMULA... I WOULD HAVE KILLED HER.

YOU HAVE THE REST OF THE FORMULA- GET RID OF IT!

AFTER ALL THE WORK WE'VE DONE? YOU CAN'T BE SERIOUS!

IT'S NOT WHAT WE THOUGHT WE WERE CREATING! IT'S EVIL, MORRIS! DESTROY IT, D'YOU HEAR?

"BUT I COULDN'T JUST THROW AWAY THE KNOWLEDGE WE'D GAINED -THE SECRET WE'D UNCOVERED. NOT WITHOUT KNOWING WHAT IT WAS LIKE TO EXPERIENCE IT..."

"BESIDES, IT WAS MINE AS MUCH AS DAVID'S. HE'D DISCOVERED THE ALCHEMIST'S MANUSCRIPT, BUT HE COULD NEVER HAVE HANDLED THE CHEMISTRY. I HAD A RIGHT TO KNOW!"

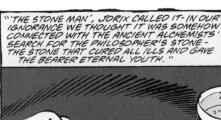

"'THE STONE MAN', JORIX CALLED IT - IN OUR IGNORANCE WE THOUGHT IT WAS SOMEHOW CONNECTED WITH THE ANCIENT ALCHEMISTS' SEARCH FOR THE PHILOSOPHER'S STONE - THE STONE THAT CURED ALL ILLS AND GAVE THE BEARER ETERNAL YOUTH. "

"WHAT WE CREATED WAS SOMETHING DIFFERENT..."

"MUCH, MUCH DIFFERENT."

"BUT IN ITS OWN WAY, NO LESS MARVELOUS.'"

THE FEELING OF IT! I CANNOT DESCRIBE IT ADEQUATELY!

THE POWER, RAW POWER SURGING THROUGH EVERY SINEW! THE HUNGER-RAVENOUS, BESTIAL, UNREASONING!

EVERY SENSE, EVERY SENSATION MAGNIFIED-AS IF EVERYTHING BEFORE HAD BEEN NOTHING BUT A...A DULL PARODY OF EXISTENCE. I WAS ALIVE, TRULY ALIVE FOR THE FIRST TIME!

I CAME FOR YOU THAT NIGHT, CHRISTINA.

IT WAS YOUR BLOOD, MORE THAN ANY OTHER, THAT I CRAVED-

"IT WAS YOUR BLOOD WE USED TO COMPLETE THE FORMULA-TO CREATE THE STONE MAN..."

"ONLY YOUR BLOOD WOULD SATE HIM!"

I SUSPECTED YOU HADN'T DESTROYED THE FORMULA, MORRIS!

WHERE IS SHEEE?

WITH FRIENDS. WHERE YOU CAN'T REACH HER.

I MUST HAVE HER! YOU MUST BRING HER TO ME!

NEVER! KEEP BACK, MORRIS, OR SO HELP ME I'LL SHOOT!

YOU CANNOT KEEP HER FROM ME!

"I WENT OUT INTO THE CITY. I FOUND TWO VICTIMS."

"THOUGH THEIR BLOOD DID NOT TOTALLY ASSUAGE MY HUNGER, THE SENSATION OF ECSTASY AS I RIPPED THEM TO SHREDS WAS ALMOST OVERPOWERING."

WE MET THAT NIGHT.

I REMEMBER.

ONLY TOO WELL.

"MY ALTERED STATE DID NOT TOTALLY BLOT OUT REASON. I RECOGNIZED YOU AS A DANGER, BATMAN."

THESE ARE DETAILS ONLY THE GARGOYLE *COULD* KNOW...

AH, YOU'RE *BEGINNING* TO *BELIEVE* ME NOW.

THE NEXT DAY DAVID BEGGED ME TO DESTROY THE FORMULA. BUT THE GARGOYLE—AS THE PRESS CAME TO CALL IT—ALREADY HAD TOO STRONG A GRIP ON ME.

I FELT SOME...*REGRET* FOR THE VICTIMS, OF COURSE—BUT IT WAS *NOTHING* TO THE URGE, THE CRAVING, TO LET HIM TAKE POSSESSION OF ME AGAIN, TO FEEL THOSE DARK DESIRES PULSING IN ME...

DAVID THREATENED TO GO TO THE AUTHORITIES AND I *LAUGHED* AT HIM. MILD-MANNERED ACADEMIC TURNS INTO A RAVING MONSTER? WHO WOULD *BELIEVE* HIM?

A FEW DAYS LATER HE SENT YOU AWAY, OUT OF MY REACH.

AND ALL THROUGH THE YEARS HE KEPT *QUIET?* CUT ME OUT OF HIS LIFE AND LET YOU GO ON *KILLING?* I—I DON'T *UNDERSTAND!* WHY DIDN'T HE JUST *TELL* SOMEONE?

BLAME THE GARGOYLE. IT GOT ITS CLAWS INTO HIM TOO. HATE IT THOUGH HE MIGHT, HE COULDN'T BRING HIMSELF TO COMMIT THAT FINAL ACT— TO DESTROY WHAT HE HAD CREATED.

BESIDES, THERE WEREN'T SO VERY MANY KILLINGS.

SIXTEEN VICTIMS ISN'T *MANY?*

YOU MAY SCOFF, BUT THERE COULD HAVE BEEN MORE, MANY MORE. BUT AFTER OUR FIRST ENCOUNTER, I KNEW I MUST BE MORE CAREFUL. I TRIED TO RATION MYSELF.

BESIDES, FAR FROM ETERNAL YOUTH, I COULD SEE THAT USE OF THE FORMULA WAS *AGING* ME...

THE INFREQUENCY PUZZLED ME. THAT'S WHAT MADE YOU SO HARD TO FIND.

I SUPPOSE EVERYTHING HAS A PRICE...

THEN YOU DECIDED TO COME HOME, CHRISTINA— THE GRAND REUNION.

"IN A WAY, YOU CAN BLAME YOURSELF FOR DAVID'S DEATH."

I'VE TRIED TO DISSUADE HER—SHE WON'T LISTEN! SHE'S DELIBERATELY ARRANGED THIS EXHIBITION AS AN EXCUSE TO BRING US TOGETHER!

IT WAS BOUND TO HAPPEN SOONER OR LATER.

IT'S FATE, DAVID. YOU MUSTN'T STAND IN ITS WAY.

COME, SHE'S HAD A GOOD LIFE. NOW SHE'S COMING HOME—TO ME ...

WHAT?

YOU KNOW IT'S ONLY RIGHT. SHE BELONGS TO ME— TO THE GARGOYLE— YOU KNOW THAT.

PERHAPS WHEN I HAVE HER THE BLOODLUST WILL DIE.

NEVER!

I SHOULD HAVE TURNED YOU IN LONG AGO! WHAT A FOOL I'VE BEEN! WELL, NO MORE!

YOU WON'T HAVE HER, MORRIS! THE REST OF THE FORMULA—GIVE IT TO ME!

NOW, COME, DAVID—

I'LL KILL YOU IF I HAVE TO!

"I COULD SEE THAT THIS TIME HE MEANT IT."

YOU GIVE ME NO CHOICE.

YOU WANT THE FORMULA—

YOU SHALL HAVE IT!

WH-WHAT'VE YOU DONE—?

"SUCH A SMALL DOSE WAS NOT ENOUGH TO EFFECT THE COMPLETE TRANSFORMATION—DAVID HAD NOT DEVELOPED THE SAME AFFINITY AS I."

"BUT THAT WORKED TO MY ADVANTAGE. THERE COULD BE NO DOUBT THAT DAVID CREIGHTON WAS THE GARGOYLE."

"HE ATTACKED ME. I FIRED IN SELF DEFENSE. WHO WOULD DOUBT ME?"

YOU MURDERED HIM!

HE GAVE ME NO OPTION. IT WAS HIM—OR THE GARGOYLE.

JUST A MINUTE DOSE...

BUT IN MY CASE QUITE AMPLE...

117

118

TONGGG TONGGG TONGGG

LISTEN!

THAT SHOOK YOU, DIDN'T IT?

TONGGG

THAT'S IT!

HOW COULD YOU KNOW—?

SOME MONTHS BACK I CAME ACROSS A PAPER BY DAVID CREIGHTON IN AN OLD SCIENTIFIC JOURNAL: "THEORIES ON THE NATURE OF THE STONE MAN".

THE CREATURE HE DESCRIBED BORN AN UNCANNY RESEMBLANCE TO THE GARGOYLE.

"I PLOTTED ALL REPORTED SIGHTINGS OF THE GARGOYLE—SIGHTINGS, NOT ATTACKS. THERE WAS A DEFINITE CONCENTRATION IN THE AREA OF THE GOTHAM INSTITUTE, WHERE CREIGHTON LIVED AND WORKED."

"SO I DUG A LITTLE DEEPER—"

"I FOUND OUT CREIGHTON HAD SENT HIS OWN DAUGHTER AWAY A FEW DAYS AFTER THE FIRST GARGOYLE KILLING. THAT MADE HIM PRIME SUSPECT."

CREIGHTON! NOT ME!

BATMAN-!

DON'T WORRY, I CAN HANDLE HIM!

CREEP GOT LUCKY THE LAST TIME... THAT'S WHY HE'S BEEN TRYING SO HARD TO STAY OUT OF MY WAY-

- DIDN'T LIKE THE IDEA OF A RETURN MATCH!

NEXT THING I KNOW THE GARGOYLE IS DEAD - AND IT *IS* CREIGHTON. SOMETHING DIDN'T ADD UP.

AT THE INQUEST IT CAME OUT THAT YOU'D WORKED ON THIS FORMULA WITH CREIGHTON. THAT MADE *YOU* PRIME SUSPECT. AND THERE WERE *FLAWS* IN YOUR TESTIMONY -

WHY WAS NONE OF THE FORMULA EVER FOUND IN CREIGHTON'S APARTMENT? AND WHY BRING A GUN TO ATTACK YOU - WHAT USE DID THE *GARGOYLE* EVER HAVE FOR A GUN?

OF COURSE, NOBODY QUESTIONED TOO DEEPLY. THEY WERE ONLY TOO WILLING TO BELIEVE THEY'D CAUGHT THE GARGOYLE AT LAST. THEY DIDN'T KNOW WHAT *I* KNEW...

"THE MISSING PART OF THE EQUATION WAS YOU."

TRANQUILIZER REALLY HITTING YOU NOW, *DOC?* GOOD! DON'T WANT TOO MUCH OF THAT "RAW POWER" ON SHOW WHEN THEY COME TO TAKE YOU AWAY!

I... I DON'T UNDERSTAND...

WE - WE'RE ALL GOING TO DIE IN HERE...

NO, WE'RE NOT. NOT EVEN *YOU*, UNFORTUNATELY.

BATMAN CAME TO SEE ME.

I WAS NEVER CALLED AS A WITNESS - I SUPPOSE THEY THOUGHT I'D HAVE NOTHING RELEVANT TO ADD, BEING SO FAR REMOVED FROM MY FATHER.

I TOLD HIM ABOUT YOUR LIE - ABOUT NOT KNOWING MY FATHER WAS THE GARGOYLE.

IT CONFIRMED MY SUSPICIONS. BUT THERE WAS NO HARD EVIDENCE AGAINST YOU. IF YOU WERE THE REAL GARGOYLE, HOW COULD WE PROVE IT?

WAIT FOR THE NEXT ATTACK? AND WHAT IF I MISSED YOU? SOME OTHER INNOCENT SLAUGHTERED - MAYBE MISS CREIGHTON?

NO... YOU HAD TO BE STOPPED, NOW - FLUSHED OUT INTO THE OPEN.

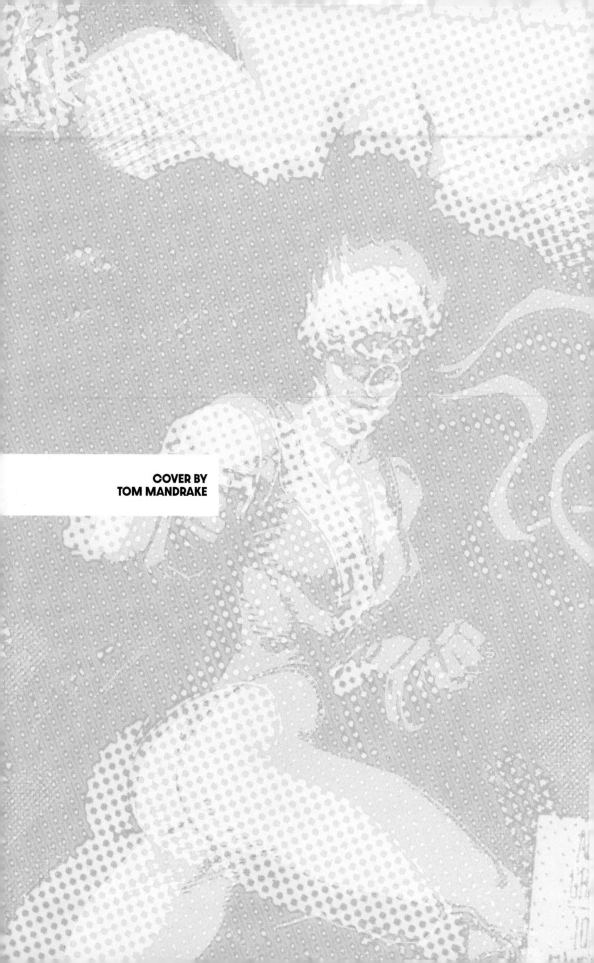

COVER BY
TOM MANDRAKE

PAGAN

TIM

MISSING BANKER FOUND NEAR-DEAD!

Gotham banker ROBERT BUICK, 2
missing for a week, was found alive
this morning. His naked body, show
clear signs of torture, had been tie
gagged and dumped in a trash car
city's docks area.

ALAN GRANT	TOM MANDRAKE	ADRIENNE ROY	JOHN COSTANZA	SCOTT PETERSON	DENNIS O'NEIL	BATMAN created by BOB KANE
writer	artist	colorist	letterer	assoc. editor	editor	

HE'S BEEN *WHIPPED*--*BEATEN*-- AND THERE ARE DEFINITE SIGNS OF SEVERE *EMOTIONAL DISTRESS!*

BUT HE'S *YOUNG.* HE'LL *SURVIVE.*

YOU CAN SEE HIM NOW. BE GENTLE... AND *BRIEF!*

THANK YOU, DOCTOR.

MR. *BUICK*... THIS IS *LIEUTENANT KITCH.* HE'D LIKE TO ASK YOU A FEW QUESTIONS.

HI. GLAD WE GOT YOU BACK IN ONE PIECE. YOU CAN THANK *BATMAN* FOR THAT. HE FOUND YOU.

SO... WHAT HAPPENED? *WAS* IT A KIDNAP? DO YOU *KNOW* WHO THEY *WERE?*

Y-YES. NO! I MEAN, I'M SORRY. I...DON'T REMEMBER!

NO MENTION OF MEMORY LOSS HERE, MR. BUICK.

YOU'RE SAYING SOMEONE *KIDNAPPED* YOU, *TORTURED* YOU FOR A WEEK --AND YOU'VE *NO* RECOLLEC- TION...?

THAT'S RIGHT! NOW GO AWAY!

LEAVE ME ALONE! I DON'T REMEMBER *ANY*THING! PLEASE-- JUST *LEAVE* ME!

GENTLEMEN...!

SORRY, NURSE. WASN'T DELIBERATE. I'LL, UH... I'LL LOOK IN LATER.

Y-YOU STAY AWAY FROM ME! I WANT A *MALE* NURSE-- A *MALE*, DO YOU HEAR?

HE WAS LYING. HE REMEMBERS, ALL RIGHT!

AGREED. COULD BE *TRAUMA*, I GUESS.

BUT UNLESS HE *TELLS* US, THERE'S NOT A WHOLE LOT FOR US TO GO ON!

LIKE, WHO WOULD KIDNAP A WEALTHY YOUNG MAN, ISSUE *NO* RANSOM DEMAND, TORTURE HIM, AND THEN JUST *DUMP* HIM LIKE A PIECE OF *TRASH?*

IF I FIND OUT--

I'LL LET YOU KNOW!

WHO KNOWS, WE MIGHT EVEN FIND YOU A GIRL!

HA HA! NO THANKS, OLLY-- I'VE HAD ENOUGH FOR TONIGHT.

CALL YOU TOMORROW!

HEYY--!

MANIAC!

WHAT THE --?

DIM THOSE LIGHTS, YOU FOOL!

AAAHH!

T-HUMMP

SCREEEE

KERAASH

131

--YES, MR. LANGAN WAS HERE EARLIER. HE LEFT TO GO HOME.

HOW? CAB?

NO, HE WAS DRIVING HIS SPORTS CAR.

YOU KNOW WHERE *"HOME"* IS?

WELL, I SHOULDN'T REALLY SAY--

HIS *LIFE* MIGHT BE AT STAKE, MAN!

"THE PENTHOUSE AT THE THORNTON BUILDING!"

SPORTS CAR?

SCREEECH

WHAT HAPPENED HERE?

STRAIGHTFORWARD ACCIDENT, LOOKS LIKE. ONLY--THERE'S NO SIGN OF THE DRIVER! PROBABLY DRUNK--*PANICKED* AND RAN OFF!

WE'LL CHECK OUT HIS HOME. IT'S REGISTERED TO PETER--

LANGAN, OF THE THORNTON BUILDING.

AND IT WAS NO ACCIDENT--

HE WAS *PUSHED* OFF THE ROAD!

LIGHT-COLORED VEHICLE-- POSSIBLY A *PICKUP.*

HOW CAN YOU TELL?

POINT OF IMPACT'S TOO HIGH FOR A CAR FENDER,

LOOKS LIKE IT WAS DAMAGED, TOO. OIL LEAK.

PROBABLY WON'T GET ME FAR--

BUT AT LEAST IT'LL POINT ME IN THE RIGHT DIRECTION!

WHAT? MR. MACHO... FAINTED?

BOB LASTED AT *LEAST* ANOTHER HALF-DOZEN BLOWS! BUT NEVER MIND--

I'LL BE HERE WHEN YOU WAKE UP!

ABANDONED!

HMMM. BLOOD ON THE ROAD-- AND SCUFFMARKS. LOOKS LIKE THEY SWITCHED VEHICLES--

OR, RATHER, *SHE* SWITCHED VEHICLES!

UU...UUUUNH!

139

BUT WE DIDN'T--! THE JUDGE *SAID* WE DIDN'T!

THE JUDGE WAS A *MAN!* HE WAS *GUARANTEED* TO BELIEVE TWO WEALTHY RESPECTABLE YUPPIES! OF *COURSE* THE UNDER-AGE DRUNK WAS *LYING!*

SHE WAS ONLY SEVENTEEN. YOU LEFT *SCARS* THAT COULD *NEVER* HEAL. YOU *STOLE* HER *LIFE!*

WH-WHAT ARE YOU GOING TO DO WITH ME...?

I'M GOING TO TEACH YOU WHAT IT'S *LIKE*, PETER...!

SHE WAS SUCH A *VIVACIOUS*, FRIENDLY GIRL. *EVERYBODY* LOVED HER!

AND THEN-- AND THEN--

THOSE *ANIMALS!* THEY *DESTROYED* HER!

THERE, LOVE. DON'T GET UPSET.

141

144

146

YOU'RE MAKING A BIG MISTAKE--!
HOW? EVERY MAN IN GOTHAM WILL FEEL SICK TO HIS GUT WHEN THEY READ WHAT I DID TO THOSE TWO!
IF IT MAKES EVEN ONE OF THEM STOP--THINK AGAIN--BEFORE HURTING A WOMAN, IT'LL HAVE BEEN WORTH IT!
YOU'VE BROKEN THE LAW, MARIAN. YOU HAVE TO PAY!
GIVE IT UP! THERE'S NOWHERE TO GO!
OH NO?
DON'T BE A FOOL! WE'RE SIX STORIES UP--!
KERRAAK

AND **I** HALF-EXPECTED **YOU** TO **ESCAPE!**

TH-THANK YOU. OH, THANKYOUTHANKYOU!

YOU HAVE NO REASON TO THANK ME, MR. LANGAN.

BUT--

I'M HANDING YOU OVER TO THE **POLICE.** AND ONE MORE THING--

--DON'T EVER THANK ME **AGAIN!**

END

148

BATMAN

480
LATE
JUNE 92

US $1.25
CAN $1.50
UK 60p

APPROVED
BY THE
COMICS
CODE
AUTHORITY

Michael Netzer

ALAN GRANT

JIM APARO

COVER BY
MICHAEL NETZER

YOUR MOTHER'S GRAVE-- *DESECRATED!* HOW COULD THEY, *TIM?*

THE *ANIMALS!* THEY'RE NOT FIT TO *SPEAK* HER NAME!

DAD--

I WANT THEM *CAUGHT,* TIM! I WANT EVERY POLICEMAN IN GOTHAM--

DAD, *PLEASE!* DON'T UPSET YOURSELF. YOU KNOW WHAT THE DOCTOR KINSOLVING SAID ABOUT GETTING OVER-EXCITED--!

DAMN THE DOCTOR! YOUR MOTHER WAS THE FINEST, BRAVEST WOMAN I'VE EVER KNOWN!

I *WON'T* LET HER MEMORY BE *SULLIED!* I--

HUU! U-HUUUU! HUU!

U-HUUU! UH-HUUNH!

IT'S ALL RIGHT, DAD. DON'T PANIC.

IT'S ALL RIGHT!

SSS SSS

THAT BETTER?

THANKS, TIM. YOU'RE A GOOD SON.

I KNOW I HAVEN'T BEEN THE FATHER I SHOULD HAVE BEEN – BUT I'LL MAKE IT UP TO YOU--

STARTING TOMORROW!

2

COME ON— WE'D BETTER GET YOU BACK...DOCTOR KINSOLVING SAID SHE WANTED TO RUN SOME FINAL CHECKS BEFORE THE BIG DAY.

Dear Dad,
I wish we could go back and start over again! When I was a kid, I used to dream - to pray - that you and mom would stop travelling, forget business and just settle down. We'd be together, the way a family ought to be...

Now I have my wish. I'm going to be with you all the time. And it's tearing me apart.

THANK GOODNESS THIS IS THE *LAST* NIGHT YOU'LL BE IMPOSING ON *BRUCE WAYNE!*

GOTHAM CITY HOSPITAL

THE MAN'S A *WOMANIZER*— A *PLAYBOY!* I DON'T LIKE YOU BEING EXPOSED TO HIS INFLUENCE!

THAT'S NOT FAIR, DAD. BRUCE IS ONE OF THE KINDEST, *MOST* DECENT PEOPLE I'VE EVER MET.

HE TOOK ME IN, DIDN'T HE, WHEN YOU AND MOM WERE IN *HAITI?* AND AFTER YOU...AFTER WHAT HAPPENED WITH *THE OBEAH MAN*— IT WAS BRUCE WHO LOOKED AFTER ME. HE'S MY *FRIEND!*

THE "AIRHEAD PLAYBOY" IMAGE IS JUST AN *INVENTION* OF THE *NEWSPAPERS!*

MAYBE— BUT *I'M* YOUR *FATHER*, TIM. *NOT* HIM!

TRY TO UNDERSTAND, SON. YOU'RE ALL I HAVE LEFT NOW. I--I DON'T WANT TO LOSE *YOU*, TOO!

TOMORROW, SON?

YES, DAD. TOMORROW.

③

MR. DRAKE? MR. MARIN TO SEE YOU.

PHIL!

HOLD ON, TIM--!

PHIL MARIN - MY SON, TIM. TIM - PHIL'S MY C.E.O. HE'S BEEN IN CHARGE AT DRAKE INDUSTRIES WHILE I'VE BEEN IN HERE.

HEARD A LOT ABOUT YOU, TIM. I'LL HAVE TO WATCH OUT FOR MY JOB. YOUR DAD TELLS ME YOU'LL BE COMING INTO THE BUSINESS... STARTING PART-TIME NEXT WEEK.

I AM?

I MEAN, OF COURSE. WHATEVER MY FATHER WANTS.

Funny, how once you never seemed to care - at least, you never showed me that you did. And now you want to run my Life.

Do you really think we can start over...?

SO...YOU WILL BE MOVING OUT, SIR?

LOOKS LIKE IT, ALFRED. HE WANTS ME TO MOVE INTO THE ROBINSON PARK PENTHOUSE WITH HIM.

NOT THE BEST OF ENVIRONMENTS FOR AN INVALID, I'D HAVE THOUGHT.

4

WELL DONE, SIR!

A LAST HURRAH, PERHAPS?

HOW DO YOU MEAN?

WELL, WITH TOMORROW AND EVERYTHING — I THOUGHT YOU MIGHT NOT BE ... GOING OUT TONIGHT.

OH NO. I'LL BE THERE!

I've no idea who you think I am, Dad — but I'm not that boy. I had to fend for myself for a long time. I changed, Dad. I have a lot of ... secrets.

-- SHOULD BE GOING OUT, DANCING, SOCIALIZING, MAKING FRIENDS!

7

I HEAR YOU, ALFRED. BUT IT WAS TIM'S OWN CHOICE TO BECOME *ROBIN.* I TRIED TO *DISSUADE* HIM, REMEMBER!

YES, SIR. I KNOW.

IT'S JUST— IT'LL BE SO MUCH *HARDER* FOR HIM, HAVING HIS FATHER TO LOOK AFTER AS WELL. THE BOY WILL NEVER HAVE A CHANCE TO LEAD EVEN A *SEMBLANCE* OF AN ORDINARY LIFE!

WHO EVER SAID LIFE WAS FAIR, ALFRED?

WHERE IS HE?

UPSTAIRS. HE SAID HE'D A LETTER TO WRITE.

I'M HERE. SORRY TO KEEP YOU.

GRRR

TAKE TONIGHT OFF IF YOU WANT.

NO. I SHOULD BE OUT THERE. IT'S MY JOB.

8

158

NO. I'D LIKE TO CHECK THE *Y-DOGS* GANG.

THOSE TWO I TOLD YOU ABOUT WERE WEARING *DESIGNER* CLOTHES— AND I'M TALKING *VERY* EXPENSIVE!

I'VE A HUNCH IT MIGHT PAY TO LOOK INTO *WHERE* THEY GOT THE *CASH..!*

You couldn't be more wrong about Bruce Wayne. Despite what he seems, he is the only truly great man I have ever known. He....*helps* people. And he *never* asks for anything in return.

I'm not interested in your business, Dad. I've already found my place in the world. I *know* what I want to be!

WOTTA COUPLE CHUMPS, ALL RIGHT!

AN' WHO DID THIS TO YA? ONE PUNY *RICH BRAT?*

HAW HAW!

GIVE US A BREAK, *RETCH!* THE CREEP... UHH, TOOK US BY SURPRISE!

WELL, YA CAN'T HANG OUT WITH THE Y-DOGS LOOKIN' LIKE *THAT!* WHERE'S YER *STYLE*, MAN?

DON'T SWEAT IT. NEXT JOB WE DO'LL SEE US RIGHT!

10

GUESS WE JUST SETTLE DOWN AN' WAIT!

I KNOW WE SHOULDN'T BRING OUR PROBLEMS ON THE JOB WITH US, BUT... DO YOU MIND IF WE *TALK?*

WON'T HURT THIS ONCE. YOUR FATHER--?

YES. THE DOCTOR SAYS IT'S HIGHLY UNLIKELY HE'LL EVER GET BETTER THAN HE IS NOW. EIGHTY PERCENT *PARALYZED.* *BREATHING* PROBLEMS.

IF I HAVE TO GO HOME AND LOOK AFTER HIM...HOW WILL I BE ABLE TO BE *ROBIN,* TOO?

HE THINKS HE'S LOSING ME-TO YOU. BUT IT'S NOT THAT. IT'S JUST... I'M *NOT* WHO HE *THINKS* I AM!

ANY SOLUTIONS?

THE ONLY ONE I CAN SEE IS - TO TELL HIM WHO I *REALLY* AM. I THINK MAYBE HE COULD COPE WITH THAT - UNDERSTAND. HE MIGHT ALLOW THINGS TO GO ON AS THEY ARE.

12

HEY, YOU'LL BE WEARING *FOUR* NEW JACKETS TOMORROW, SCRUFF!

DRAKE MED? THAT'S ONE OF *DAD'S* COMPANIES!

DO WE TAKE THEM?

NO. THEY'LL BE HERE LATER. WE CAN COME BACK.

HEY, IS THAT ALL?

PAY AS YOU GO, PAL!

THIRTY MINUTES! BE HERE!

So how does it sound, Dad? Your own son is Robin. Understand now why I can't come back? Gotham is a cesspool. Tragedy stalks on every street. I can help, dad. I'm needed!

14

STOP HIM, ROBIN!

KEEP BACK, BRAT! I'M WARNING YOU--!

KRANG

WAKK

BAPP

16

NEAT!

THE POLICE CAN TAKE IT FROM HERE.

COME ON. I'LL TAKE YOU HOME. TOMORROW'S A BIG DAY.

HOME?

NO. I'D LIKE TO MAKE MY OWN WAY TONIGHT.

17

I'LL TAKE CARE OF THE Y-DOGS!

Sometimes I wish we could start over... but I know we can't. We have to take things from exactly where we are.

TIM..?

UPSTAIRS, SIR. SAID HE HAD A LETTER TO FINISH.

GOOD MORNING.

HI.

THAT MATTER WE WERE DISCUSSING LAST NIGHT... WE DIDN'T GET TO FINISH.

IT'S ALL RIGHT. I'VE SORTED IT OUT.

I'VE NEVER FELT I WAS PART OF A *FAMILY* BEFORE. THAT'S SOMETHING I'LL ALWAYS BE GRATEFUL TO YOU FOR, BRUCE — AND YOU, ALFRED.

BUT MY *FATHER'S* MY FAMILY, TOO. HE NEEDS ME.

WOULD YOU MIND RUNNING ME TO THE HOSPITAL, ALFRED? DAD'LL BE MAD IF I KEEP HIM WAITING!

RIGHT AWAY, SIR!

I'LL SEE YOU SOON. MAYBE NOT TONIGHT. BUT SOON.

I LOOK FORWARD TO IT!

20

I THOUGHT THE COUNTRY AIR MIGHT BE GOOD FOR YOUR FATHER'S HEALTH.

FOR SALE
SPACIOUS MANSION IN TOO WOODED ACRES CLOSE TO GOTHAM CITY
—
GOTHAM REALTY CO
TON AVENUE · (212) 879·1700

INTEREST RATES 5%

AND OF COURSE, AS IT'S RIGHT NEXT DOOR TO MASTER BRUCE'S...

WELL, IT MIGHT BE GOOD FOR YOURS, TOO!

I'LL WORK ON HIM, ALFRED. I PROMISE — I'LL WORK ON HIM!

END/

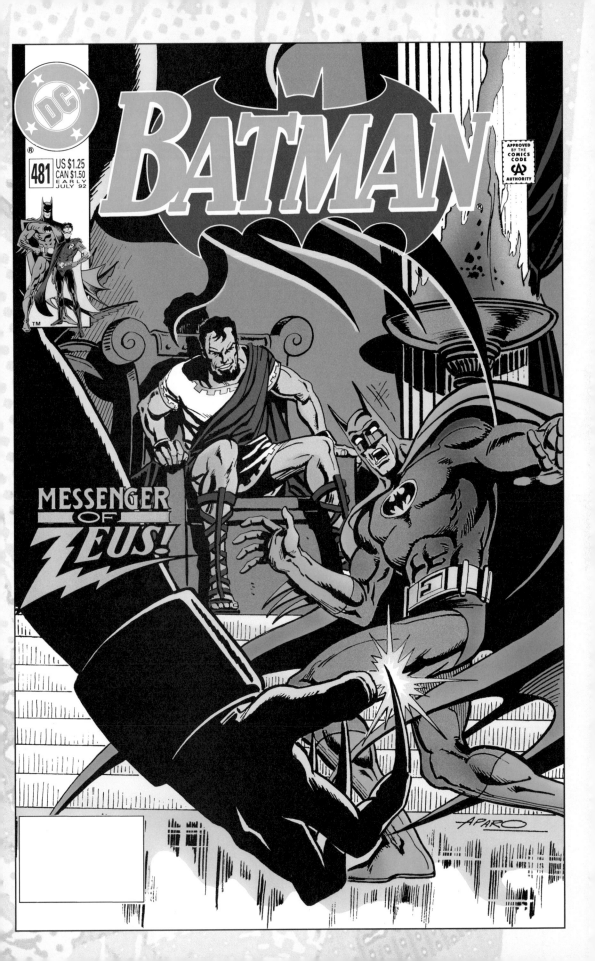

COVER BY
JIM APARO

... I WILL BEAR YOUR MESSAGE AT *ONCE,* LORD ZEUS.

KLIK

WE *CAN'T* CURE. AT BEST, WE CAN MERELY *CONTAIN.*

GOTHAM

THE CLOUD ROOM

MAXIE'S *WHACKO* -- AND HE'S *ALWAYS* HAD A THING FOR THE *BATMAN.*

-- CALLED IT *"A BOX FOR THE BATMAN,"* CAN YOU BELIEVE *THAT?*

ME, I DON'T CARE *WHAT* HE CALLED IT -- I *WANT* IT.

GONZO, JOHNNY, TURK, RUBE -- CATCH YOU GENTS *LATER,* HUH?

WHAT'S HARD TO BELIEVE--?

WE UNDERSTAND, *ACE...*

...YOU BABIES NEED PLENTY OF *SLEEP.*

3

ONE LEAVING...

...AND AN EASY ONE TO CRACK.

PAF

"BABY," HUH?

THE CLOUD ROOM

SHYIIIH...

PAF

TWUNG

K-CHAK

4

BUT *WE* WANT IT BECAUSE THE *STUPID* THING IS WORTH A WHOLE WARE-HOUSE OF *MODERN* SWAG.

PRECISELY, RUBE...

... WHICH IS WHY WE'VE *GOTTA* GO THROUGH WITH THE JOB.

WITH MAXIE IN THE *NUTHATCH,* WE CAN CASH THE THING *IN* -- INSTEAD O' *DUSTIN'* AN' *POLISHIN'* IT EVERY TEN MINUTES FOR HIS *LORDLY GAZE.*

NO!!

WHAT THE--?

WHO--?

IRIS--?

AND SHE FINALLY *FLIPPED ALL THE WAY* -- WENT BACK TO HER ROOTS AS A *SWING-GIRL...*

I BEAR A MESSAGE FROM *LORD ZEUS* --

-- A MESSAGE DESIGNED TO ENSURE YOUR *WELL-BEING* --

-- AND I FIND YOU CONSPIRING TO *BETRAY* ZEUS BE-HIND HIS *BACK!*

BAMP

7

"JUST A *DAME,*" HUH--¿

THEY'LL FIND OUT...

THEY'LL LEARN THE *TRUE MEANING* OF FURY...

ARE YOU SPEAKING TO--

YOUR *HEAD*-- IT'S BLEEDING...

...AND SUFFER... THE CONSEQUENCES...

I THINK YOU NEED *HELP*-- YOU'D BETTER COME INTO MY *OFFICE.*

ZEUS TRIED TO *PROTECT* THEM... FROM THE DWELLER OF *HADES*... AND THEY *BETRAYED* HIM...

SHONDRA KINSOLVING M.D. PHYSICAL THERAPIST

--EVIDENTLY HAD PLANNED SOME CRIME BEFORE HIS COMMIT- MENT HERE AT ARKHAM, PERHAPS TO BE CARRIED OUT BY THOSE MEMBERS OF HIS GANG STILL AT LARGE.

EASY... JUST TAKE IT EASY.

YES...

...I'D GOTTEN WIND OF AS MUCH ON MY *OWN.*

AH.

WELL, INASMUCH AS YOU ARE REPEATEDLY MENTIONED IN *CONNECTION* WITH THIS PLANNED CRIME, I THOUGHT IT MY DUTY --PERHAPS MY *LAST* OFFICIAL DUTY -- TO LET YOU *HEAR THE TAPE.*

11

AND YOU *ACQUIRED* THIS TAPE...?

THROUGH ELECTRONIC SURVEILLANCE.

KLIK

FOR THE INMATES' *OWN PROTECTION*, IF NOTHING ELSE.

THE MESSAGE IS *THIS*, IRIS. THE *DUST-BUCKET* CAN WAIT.

IT MUST *WAIT*! DO YOU *UNDERSTAND*, IRIS? TELL THEM *NOT TO GO THROUGH WITH IT*! IT IS *DOOMED*!

--NOTHING *SERIOUS*, ALTHOUGH YOU MAY HAVE A SLIGHT CONCUSSION.

I'D LIKE TO CHECK YOU INTO THE HOSPITAL FOR OVERNIGHT OBSERVATION...

NO.

THANK YOU FOR YOUR MINISTRATIONS, BUT I AM *FINE* NOW...

I'M CLEAR...I'M *PERFECTLY* CLEAR.

IRIS IS *DEAD* NOW... AND I HAVE A *NEW* MISSION...

SHONDRA KINSOLVING M.D. PHYSICAL THERAPIS

...FROM *MESSENGER* OF ZEUS... TO *AVENGER* OF ZEUS.

12

EVENING OF THE FOLLOWING DAY...

FOR SALE

I REALLY WISH I COULD HAVE GOTTEN YOU OUT HERE *EARLIER,* AND I *DO* APOLOGIZE FOR THE DELAY, BUT THERE *IS* JUST ENOUGH LIGHT TO VIEW THE *EXTERIOR...*

YEAH, LOOKS GREAT--*DOESN'T* IT, DAD?

NHN.

I THINK WE'RE GONNA *LIKE* IT HERE, DAD.

WE HAVEN'T EVEN SEEN THE *INSIDE* YET, TIM.

WHY ARE YOU *SO SET* ON--

SKREEEE

EH--? THERE ARE *BATS?*

HEY, WE'RE OUTSIDE THE *CITY* NOW, DAD-- IT'S PRACTICALLY THE *COUNTRY* OUT HERE.

THAT'S WHERE BATS *LIVE.*

BUT A *BAT* IS--

NOT SO BAD ONCE YOU GET TO KNOW HIM... GET *USED* TO 'EM, I MEAN.

WELL, LET ME SHOW YOU FOLKS THE *INTERIOR*--IT'S IN *EXCELLENT* CONDITION...

13

THEY THINK THEY CAN FEAST ON THE SPOILS OF LORD ZEUS'S *MISFORTUNE*...

...BUT IT WILL BE *THEIR* MISFORTUNE WHEN THE FEAST IS *SPOILED*.

YOU'VE BEEN AT IT *ALL DAY,* SIR...

WHATEVER THE PLANNED CAPER *IS,* ALFRED, IT COULD COME OFF AT ANY TIME...

...AND IT'S JUST ABOUT *DARK* AGAIN.

...EVEN TONIGHT.

-- DUST-BUCKET MUST WAIT!

BUT I JUST CAN'T PUZZLE OUT THIS *"DUST-BUCKET"* REFERENCE...

DO TRY TO *EAT,* SIR, WHILE YOU PUZZLE?

14

-- SUPPOSE IT'LL DO... AND THE *TERMS* SEEM GENERALLY FAIR... BUT I WANT TO GO OVER *ALL* THE *DETAILS.*

EVERYTHING WE NEED IS RIGHT IN *HERE,* MR. DRAKE.

NHN.

I THINK I'LL TAKE A LITTLE *WALK* WHILE YOU TWO TALK IT OVER...

YOU KNOW, CHECK OUT THE *GROUNDS.*

ALL RIGHT, TIM, BUT DON'T BE *LONG* -- AND BE *CAREFUL* OUT THERE.

DAUGHTER OF *THAUMAS* AND *ELECTRA*... THY *FURY* SHALL RIDE THE WINDS.

I... I THINK DAD'S GONNA GO FOR IT.

HM? OH... GOOD NEWS, TIM.

YOU *ONTO* SOMETHING?

YES.

... MAXIE ZEUS'S GANG... SOME-THING ABOUT A "DUST-BUCKET"!..

KLIK

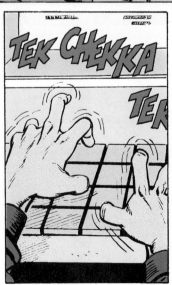

TEK CHEKKA TER

COULD THAT "*DUST-BUCKET*" OF YOURS REFER TO A *PRICELESS* GREEK *FUNERARY* URN, CIRCA 435 BC?

EH?? *FUNERARY* URN--?

15

RIGHT ON THE *VERY NEXT PAGE...*

ASHES TO ASHES... *DUST TO DUST...*

HOW'D YOU COME *UP* WITH THAT SO FAST, TIM?

JUST HACKED INTO TICKETRON AND FOUND A SPECIAL EXHIBIT COMING TO *GOTHAM MUSEUM* -- RARE GREEK ARTIFACTS, INCLUDING A FUNERARY URN.

STARTS TOMORROW.

WHICH MEANS IT'LL BE IN PLACE *TONIGHT.*

YOU, UH, MAYBE NEED SOME *HELP?*

I DON'T THINK SO...

RIGHT NOW, SON, MAYBE IT'S TIME YOU WORRIED ABOUT YOUR *REAL* FATHER.

VROOOM

LIKE I HAVEN'T BEEN DOING *NOTHING* BUT.

16

THE *ALARM SYSTEM!*

SOMEBODY--

AHN--!

SLPT

ALL RIGHT, LET'S ROLL-- *FAST* AND *SWEET.*

SPECIAL EXHIBIT GLORY OF GREECE

GOTHAM MUSEUM

SKREEE

⒘

AHRRR!

SHRREPT

THE *BATMAN TOO*--?!

WHA--?

WAKT

BAM

CHOK

GUH-H!

WE'RE DEAD.

THE *BAT-DEMON*?!
HE WHO DEFEATED
AND SHACKLED
LORD ZEUS?!

THRAK

BUT *NOW* YOU SHALL
SUFFER THE
VENGEANCE
OF THE
HARPY!

POK

POK POK POK

THERE *WAS* NO TRAP--
BUT THIS MAY BE
WORSE.

WIKT TAK WAKT TIKT

20

NEXT: MADNESS OF THE HARPY

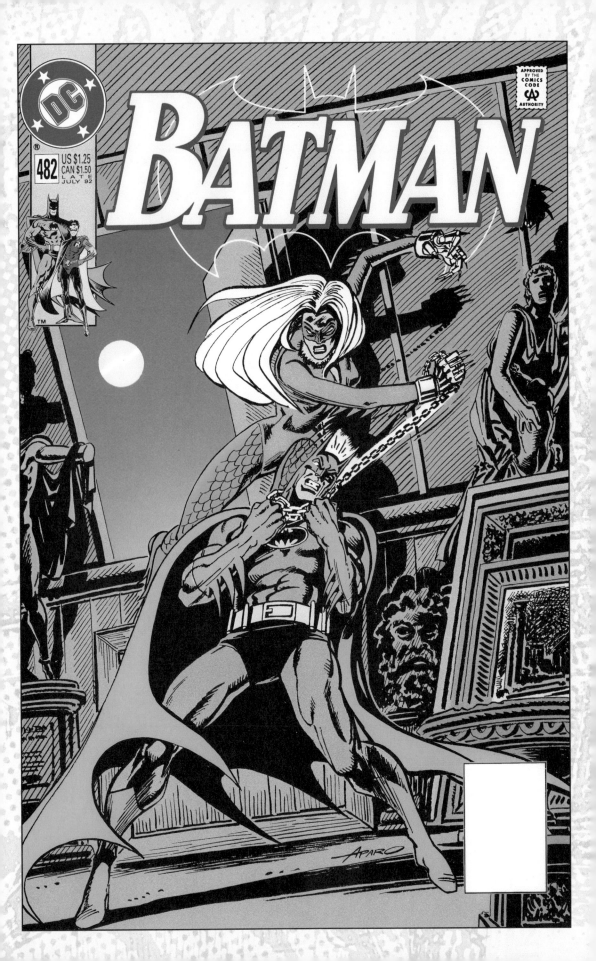

COVER BY
JIM APARO

GOTHAM MUSEUM, NIGHT:

BECAUSE OF *YOU*, BAT-DEMON, LORD ZEUS *ROTS IN HADES*.

BUT HIS *VENGEANCE* IS MINE, AND *MINE* IS THE --

VENGEANCE OF THE HARPY

DOUG MOENCH	JIM APARO	ADRIENNE ROY	SCOTT PETERSON	DENNY O'NEIL	BOB KANE
WRITER	ART/LETTERS	COLORIST	ASST. EDITOR	EDITOR	CREATOR

PAF

REPT

--BEFORE THAT DAZED *NIGHT GUARD* EVEN KNEW WHAT *HIT* HIM.

BUT THE *HARPY,* NO DOUBT, IS ALREADY--

"--GONE."

MORNING...

GOTHAM MUSEUM

FEELS LIKE SUMMER'S COMIN' EARLY, MONTOYA...

IF YOU SAY SO, SERGEANT.

4

YOU DON'T *FEEL* IT?

NO.

ASK ME, IT'S HOTTER'N A *SATURDAY NIGHT TAMALE* IN TIJUANA... IF YA CATCH MY *DRIFT*.

I'D RATHER *NOT*.

NOW WHAT'VE WE *GOT* HERE?

THEFT, MONTOYA-- ONE OF THE STAR PIECES IN A TRAVELING EXHIBIT FROM *GREECE*.

SPECIAL EXHIBIT GLORY OF GREECE

AND THIS "STAR PIECE"-- NO COMMENTS FROM *YOU*, SERGEANT BULLOCK-- WAS EXACTLY *WHAT*?

ANCIENT *FUNERARY URN.* GUESS THEY BURNED 'EM BACK THEN.

ANY LEADS?

FORENSICS IS STILL DUSTIN' FOR PRINTS, BUT WHO-EVER IT WAS, THEY MUST BE *GOOD*-- GOOD ENOUGH SO'S THE *BATMAN* COULDN'T STOP 'EM.

THE *BATMAN*?

THAT'S *HIS LINE* UP THERE, BULLOCK-- PREVENTIN' YOU FROM BEIN' *CRUSHED* BY YOUR COUSIN.

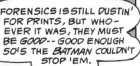

GULMP

5

THE CLOUD ROOM

NEXT TIME THAT "HARPY" SHOWS UP WILL BE TROUBLE.

I SAY WE CUT NEXT TIME OFF AT THE PASS.

GOOD IDEA, TURK-- YOU HANDLE IT.

LUCKY FOR US CRAZY IRIS DID SHOW UP LAST NIGHT. IF NOT FOR HER, THE BATMAN WOULDA NAILED US BEFORE WE LAID A FINGER ON THIS URN.

YEAH, BUT THAT KINDA LUCK DON'T HAPPEN TWICE...

YOU MEAN... WHACK HER?

SHE WANTS TO WHACK US, DON'T SHE?

YEAH, BUT...I MEAN, SHE MAY BE PSYCHO NOW, CALLIN' HERSELF THE HARPY IN THAT SCREWY GET-UP AN' ALL, BUT SHE'S STILL, LIKE, MAXIE ZEUS'S BABE, AIN'T SHE?

WHAT MAXIE DON'T KNOW WHILE HE'S IN THE NUT HATCH...

...WON'T HURT HIM IN THE NUT HATCH.

TURK, GET MOVIN' ON IT, AN' TAKE RUBE WITH YA-- HOLD HIS HAND, IF NEED BE.

JOHNNY, YOU STASH THIS THING IN THE SAFE TILL WE FIND A BUYER.

RIGHT, GONZ-- ONE DEEP-FRIED HARPY COMIN' UP.

6

I KNOW WHO THE THIEVES *ARE*, ALFRED -- MAXIE ZEUS'S GANG -- AND WHERE TO *FIND* THEM.

BUT YOU'RE NOT GOING TO PICK THEM *UP?*

NOT YET. WITHOUT EVIDENCE, IT'S ONLY *MY WORD AGAINST THEIRS...*

...AND THEY KNOW I'M NOT LIKELY TO *TESTIFY IN COURT.*

DEFENSE ATTORNEYS STILL INSISTING ON *FULL IDENTIFICATION* OF PROSECUTION WITNESSES, ARE THEY?

PITY, THAT.

IN ANY CASE, THE *HARPY* IS THE GREATER AND MORE IMMEDIATE THREAT -- *VIOLENTLY* INSANE.

BUT YOU *DON'T* KNOW WHERE TO FIND *HER?*

I ONLY KNOW THEY CALLED HER *IRIS.*

I'M SURE YOU'LL FIND A WAY, SIR, AND MEANWHILE THERE *IS* SOME *BRIGHT* NEWS -- OUR NEW NEIGHBORS MOVE IN *MONDAY.*

THEN TIM'S FATHER *IS* BUYING THE ESTATE?

THEY SIGN THE DOCUMENTS *TODAY.*

-- SIGNED HER *DEATH WARRANT* THE MINUTE SHE JUMPED ON OUR *DINNER TABLE,* RUBE.

YEAH, BUT... BUT MAYBE IRIS WON'T EVEN COME *BACK* HERE, TURK...

7

--MY *LAST* DAY, YOU KNOW.

YOU PROBABLY *NEED* THE REST.

YES. NOT THAT MADNESS IS *CONTAGIOUS*, OF COURSE, BUT AFTER *SO* MANY YEARS IN ITS PROXIMITY...WELL, LET'S JUST SAY SOME *DISTANCE* WILL DO ME *GOOD*.

HAVE YOU COME TO *GLOAT?* TO SEE HOW THE MIGHTY *ZEUS* HAS FALL--

MAXIE, WHAT DO YOU KNOW ABOUT A... *HARPY?*

THE *NEW DIRECTOR* ARRIVES TOMORROW. *JEREMIAH ARKHAM*, SCION OF THE ORIGINAL FAMILY.

CAN'T SAY I'M *TOO* UPSET ABOUT RETIRING...

ANYWAY, HERE HE *IS* -- JUST GIVE A CALL WHEN YOU WANT *OUT*.

A HARPY? DAUGHTER OF *THAUMAS* AND *ELECTRA*, OF COURSE -- A *TEMPEST-GODDESS*, A *RAVAGER*, SPOILER OF *FEAST*...

THERE'S A HARPY IN *GOTHAM*, MAXIE-- AND SHE'S VERY JEALOUS OF *IRIS*.

IRIS? MY *MESSENGER?*

THE HARPY WANTS TO...*TAKE HER PLACE*.

YOU MEAN... *KILL* HER?

WITH YOU IN *HERE*, MAXIE, I'M THE ONLY ONE WHO CAN *STOP* THIS HARPY... BUT I NEED TO KNOW WHERE IRIS *IS*.

IT'S A *TRICK*, ISN'T IT? A *TRAP!* YOU JUST WANT TO--

SUIT YOURSELF. IF YOU DON'T BELIEVE THE HARPY IS *REAL* --

WAIT! HER NAME IS *IRIS PHELIOS*. SHE LIVES ON *ISLAND AVENUE* -- NUMBER *489*, TOP FLOOR.

AND IF SHE'S NOT *THERE*, WHERE WOULD SHE GO?

GO? SHE'S GOT NOWHERE ELSE -- NOT SINCE I GOT HER OUT OF THE *CIRCUS*...

9

GORDON? GET A HOMICIDE TEAM DOWN TO *489 ISLAND AVENUE,* TOP FLOOR.

TWO DOWN -- BOTH MEMBERS OF *MAXIE ZEUS'S* GANG.

AND THE *MURDERER?*

THE ONE I *TOLD* YOU ABOUT-- FROM THE *MUSEUM.*

HER REAL NAME IS *IRIS PHELIOS.* THIS IS HER APARTMENT.

THE "HARPY"?

I'M GOING AFTER HER NOW.

JUST A WOMAN, AM I?

I AM THE *TEMPEST*... THE *RAVAGER*... THE *FURY* OF THE LORD'S VENGEANCE...

ONE MORE MORTAL, AND THEN THE *WORST* FOR LAST... THE *BAT-DEMON* ITSELF.

CLEARLY, SHE'S STILL AFTER THE FOUR IN THE MUSEUM, HUNTING THEM DOWN FOR "DEFYING THE WILL OF ZEUS"-- AND SHE'S ALREADY TAKEN *TWO...*

...MAKING HER *NEXT* VICTIMS OBVIOUS.

-- *SLASHED* TO DEATH.

YEAH, ALMOST LIKE AN *ANIMAL* DID IT... SOME *BEAST* OF PREY...

THREE DOWN...

"...AND ONLY *ONE LEFT.*" JOHNNY SPLATTERED OUT IN THE *STREET...* TURK AN' *KUBE* NOT ANSWERIN' THEIR *PHONES...*

I GOTTA GET *OUT* O' HERE WHILE I *CAN...*

...*SELL* THIS THING FOR A LONG TICKET OUTTA *TOWN.*

LEAVING *EARLY* TONIGHT, SIR?

UH, YEAH...

CLOUD ROOM

MENU

12

13

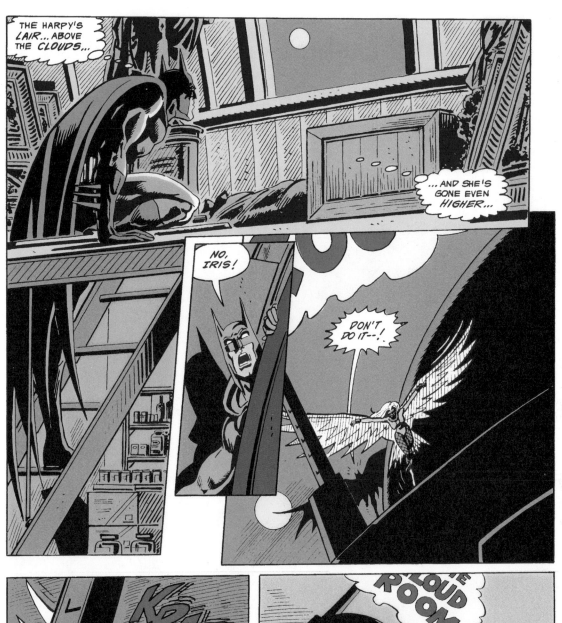

I WILL *NOT* BE SAVED BY THE *BAT-DEMON* FROM--

CHAT

UHNNNN--

EASY, IRIS-- ZEUS IS WAITING FOR YOU...

...ALTHOUGH *HARDLY* IN OLYMPUS.

QUITE A NIGHT... BUT WHY DID MAXIE ZEUS *WANT* THIS ITEM IN THE FIRST PLACE? SIMPLY TO *SELL?*

ACCORDING TO ONE OF HIS GANG, IT WAS SUPPOSED TO BE FOR *ME.*

A *GIFT?*

ONLY *POSTHUMOUSLY.* IT'S A *FUNERARY URN,* GORDON...

...INTENDED FOR *MY* ASHES.

END

DC

BATMAN

483
AUG 92

US $1.25
CAN $1.50
UK 60p

APPROVED BY THE COMICS CODE AUTHORITY

HANNIGAN/APARO

DOUG MOENCH

JIM APARO

INTRODUCING...

CRASH & BURN!

COVER BY
ED HANNIGAN AND JIM APARO

CRASH & BURN
A LOVE STORY

MAYBE IT WAS THE WAY HE CAME INTO MY LIFE, COUPLED WITH THE QUIRK OF MY OWN NAME. OR MAYBE MY FATHER REALLY *WAS* TO BLAME—IN BOTH WAYS, GENETICS *AND* ENVIRONMENT.

THEN AGAIN MAYBE IT WAS PURE GREED—OR SOME INFECTION OF EVIL, WITH OR WITHOUT THE "D" IN FRONT OF IT.

BUT PROBABLY IT WAS JUST BOREDOM.

DOUG MOENCH	JIM APARO	ADRIENNE ROY	SCOTT PETERSON	DENNIS O'NEIL	BOB KANE
WRITER	ART / LETTERS	COLORIST	ASST. EDITOR	EDITOR	CREATOR

HE CAME OUT OF THE FOUR-BY-FOUR LIKE SOME SPRINGSHOT JUNGLE BRUTE ON DOUBLE STEROIDS.

EVERYBODY *DOWN!* NO ALARMS, NO BOOBYTRAPS, NO *MARKED CASH!*

MY KNEES WENT A BIT WEAK, BUT THEY DIDN'T BUCKLE...

AND *NO STUPIDITY!*

BAOUM

AHRRR

...CERTAINLY NOT LIKE THE GUARD'S.

STILL, THAT'S WHEN I KNEW...

YOU-- THE *CASH--* UNMARKED-- AND *MOVE IT!*

...IT WAS *HEAT AT FIRST SIGHT.*

IT'S NOT THAT IT SEEMED LIKE THE *RIGHT* THING TO DO.

IT WAS SUDDENLY THE *ONLY* THING...

SEE, HE WAS JUST THE SPARK I NEEDED TO *BURN.*

NOT SO *FAST,* CRASH. THERE MIGHT BE A *PAINT-BOMB* IN HERE.

MAKE ME *CARRY* IT FOR YOU--AS A GESTURE OF *GOOD FAITH.*

YOU *CRAZY?*

YOU *BET.*

JUST LIKE *YOU,* CRASH.

HE DIDN'T KNOW WHAT TO MAKE OF ME, AND I LIKED THAT-- *POWER* OVER SUCH POWER.

YOU EVEN *LOOK* AT ME CROOKED...

... AND YOUR HAIR GETS A *LOT* REDDER.

PROMISES, PROMISES.

AND *HURRY* UP IF YOU'RE COMIN'!

UH-*UH*--FIRST I HAVE TO PUT IN MY *RESIGNATION.*

JANET BYRNE,

FLTCH

JANET BYRNE

THOSE WERE THE *MARKED* BILLS.

HE NEVER LAUGHED -- NO SENSE OF HUMOR -- BUT IT WAS HIS FIRST *REAL* SMILE, AND IT'D DO.

NOT *THAT* ONE, BYRNE -- I JUST STOLE IT FOR THE *JOB*.

RIGHT.

SO LONG, SHIRLEY, EDNA...DOUBT I'LL BE WRITING, BUT DON'T FORGET TO CALL AN AMBULANCE FOR *FRANK* THERE.

THE *RED* PORSCHE, BYRNE.

BAOUM

BANK OF MIAMI

POLICE

BANK

SKREEEE

SKRASH

...'CEPT *THESE* ARE STOLEN *TOO*.

SKREEEE

I STARTED LAUGHING AND KEPT IT UP TILL IT WASN'T FUNNY ANYMORE.

BETTER WHEELS THAN THE ONES YOU *STOLE*, CRASH.

YEAH...

FWHOOM

WE CLEARED MIAMI BY SUNSET, BUT I WAS STILL LAUGHING AND CRASH HAD TO SLUG ME BEFORE I COULD STOP.

IT GOT TOO QUIET THEN, SO HE PULLED OVER AND KISSED ME. I WANTED TO LAUGH AGAIN, MAYBE FOREVER, BUT INSTEAD I CRIED. AND THAT'S HOW IT STARTED BETWEEN US, LAUGHTER AND TEARS FOR ME, DEAD SILENCE FROM HIM.

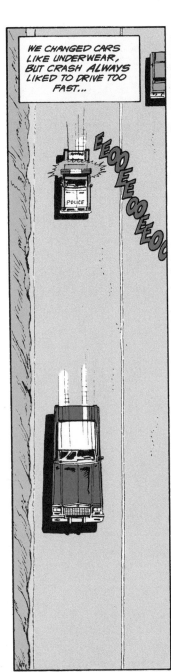

WE CHANGED CARS LIKE UNDERWEAR, BUT CRASH ALWAYS LIKED TO DRIVE TOO FAST...

...WAY TOO FAST, LIKE ANYTHING UNDER A HUNDRED WAS SOME KIND OF CRIPPLED BABY'S CRAWL.

CAN I SEE YOUR LI--

BAOUM

HE NEVER DID LEARN TO SLOW DOWN.

SKREEEE

I THINK THAT'S WHAT I LOVED ABOUT HIM, EVEN IF HE COULDN'T LAUGH.

WE WEREN'T BIG ON THE FUTURE, CRASH OR ME, BUT SOONER OR LATER IT HAD TO REAR UP AND SPIT AT US.

YOU JUST TURNED BAD, BYRNE.

I WAS ALREADY BAD, CRASH...

...WANTIN' TO RIP THAT BANK EVER SINCE THEY SLAPPED MY NAME-TAG ON.

I JUST NEED A GOOD SPARK, BABY, THAT'S ALL I EVER NEED.

DO MY BEST.

YOU ALREADY HAVE, CRASH. I WON'T NEVER FLAME OUT NOW, NOT TILL THE END.

TOLD YOU NOT TO TALK ABOUT--

ALL RIGHT.

SO... WHERE WE HEADED?

THEY SAY HELL'S SOUTH.

FIGURE WE'LL KEEP GOIN' NORTH -- TO THE BIG CITY.

GOTHAM?

YEAH.

HARDLY HEAVEN.

PROB'LY NOT, BYRNE... BUT AS GOOD A PLACE AS ANY TO CRASH.

KCHAK

SEE, THAT'S THE THING ABOUT THE FUTURE -- IT'S HARD TO AVOID.

WE KEPT HEADING NORTH ANYWAY...

AND HOW WOULD YOU LIKE THAT?

TWENTIES AND TENS WILL BE--

...WITH STOPS ALONG THE WAY.

BLASHH

WE'RE CRASH AND BURN! DO YOURSELVES A FAVOR AND DON'T DO AS WE DO!

DO AS WE SAY--AND LIVE A WHILE!

EVERYBODY DOWN!!

NO ALARMS, NO BOOBY-TRAPS, AND NO MARKED BILLS!

I... P-PLEASE...

SHUT UP AND STUFF THAT MONEY!

CRASH HAD BEEN IN THE SPECIAL FORCES, WHERE KNOWLEDGE OF INCENDIARY DEVICES WAS CONSIDERED ESSENTIAL...

LET'S FLY, BURN!

FLTCH

...AND I'D BEEN TO A DOZEN MOTELS, WHERE I PROVED TO BE A QUICK STUDY.

WE MADE A GOOD PAIR, A CLASSIC TEAM...

EEEEEEEE

FWOOOSH

...TIGHT AND RIGHT, LIKE BREAD AND BUTTER.

--SOUND WORSE THAN *BONNIE AND CLYDE.*

THEY SEEM BENT ON *SUICIDE*, COMMISSIONER, AS IF THEY KNOW THEY'RE DOOMED AND JUST WANT TO GO OUT IN *FLAMES*...

BUT SO FAR NO ONE'S BEEN ABLE TO ACCOMMODATE THEM IN *SIX* STATES.

HNH.

MORE *RUTHLESS* AND *BRUTAL*, THAT'S FOR CERTAIN...

G.C.P.D.

OTHER THAN WHAT YOU'VE ALREADY TOLD ME ABOUT THEIR *M.O.*, MONTOYA, WHAT *ELSE* IS KNOWN ABOUT THEM?

NOT MUCH--UNKNOWN MALE AND A FEMALE ACCOMPLICE NAMED *JANET BYRNE*.

THE *"BURN"* OF CRASH AND BURN.

A *BANK TELLER* WHO JOINED HIM IN THE MIDDLE OF A MIAMI *ROBBERY*.

AND BEST FOR LAST, COMMISSIONER-- THEY'RE ON A CRASH- COURSE FOR *GOTHAM*.

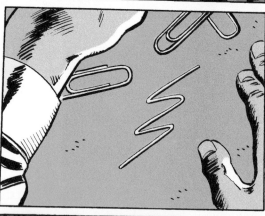

FIGURES.

WE SELDOM STOPPED MOVING, BURNING A LOT OF FUEL, AND SOMETIMES I FELT LIKE A MOTH, THE GAS STATIONS SPLASHES OF IRRESISTIBLE LIGHT.

TANK'S STILL HALF-FULL.

JOE'S SERVICE CENTER

GAS

WAY *I* SEE IT, CRASH, IT'S HALF-*EMPTY*.

CHRASH!

WHUH--?

YOUR *MONEY*-- *FAST!* AND *OPEN THE PUMPS!*

LET'S *FLY*, BURN.

FSHSHSHSHSH

CHUNK

CHUNK

233

SOCIAL STUDIES.

WHY CAN'T IT BE SOMETHING LESS *BORING*, LIKE COMPUTER ALGORITHMS OR—

DEET-DEET

YEAH?

YOU CATCH A NAP?

RIGHT AFTER SCHOOL.

YOUR FATHER?

ASLEEP NOW.

UP FOR A RIDE?

PRAYING FOR ONE.

SOONER OR LATER, OF COURSE, CRASH'S DRIVING WAS *BOUND* TO GET US IN TROUBLE...

FIVE MINUTES INTO GOTHAM IS WHERE IT DID.

CRASH! LOOK OUT!!

JUST BEFORE IT HAPPENED I FIGURED IT WAS OUR TIME, A REAL STUPID WAY TO GO, BUT AT LEAST A BIG CRASH.

I WAS WRONG. WE BOTH WOKE UP STILL ALIVE -- ASLEEP FOR ONLY SECONDS.

WON'T TURN OVER... MUST'VE MASHED THE BATTERY...

P-POP... THE TRUNK...

THE *HEAT*, CRASH!

KEEP MOVIN'-- EVERYBODY OFF THE BUS!

MOVE IT, MOVE IT!

≩KSSST≩ --COMMANDEERED BUS ON *YORK*, SOUTHBOUND PAST *SHREVE STREET...* ≩KSSST≩

≩KSSST≩--MALE AND FEMALE, MATCHING THE *"CRASH AND BURN"* BANKROBBERS... ≩KSSST≩

SKREEEEEEE

THIS IS *IT*, HUH? GONNA CRASH FOR *GOOD* NOW-- FOR THE *LAST TIME...*

GOTHAM

AND BURN IN *HELL*, BABE.

EEOOEEEOOOE *OOEEOOEE*

AT LEAST WE'LL BE *TOGETHER*, CRASH.

824

GOTHAM BUS LINE

POLICE

POLICE

BUT HE STILL DIDN'T LAUGH.

NOT MUCH MORE TO IT. WE SETTLED IN TO WAIT. IF THE COPS HAD ANY GUTS, IT WOULDN'T BE LONG.

--SECURITY GUARD WAS DOING HIS OUTSIDE ROUNDS --ON THE OTHER SIDE OF THE BUILDING WHEN THEY CRASHED IN-- SO HE'S SAFE, BUT THE CITY...

THEY KNOW IT'S OVER, COMMISSIONER. THEY WANT US TO GO IN AND TAKE THEM DOWN--

--SO THEY CAN GO OUT IN A BLAZE OF "GLORY" RATHER THAN FACE PRISON.

TAKING A SLEW OF OUR PEOPLE WITH THEM. I DON'T LIKE IT, BUT THERE'S NO TIME TO EVACUATE... AND IF THAT CHEMICAL PLANT GOES UP, THE TOXIC FUMES WILL--

HOLD YOUR PEOPLE BACK, GORDON...

...UNTIL THERE'S NO OTHER CHOICE.

WE NEVER DID GET OUR TATTOOS, CRASH...

TIK TIK TIK

HIS WAS GOING TO READ: "DIE YOUNG"-- AND MINE WOULD'VE BEEN: "STAY PRETTY."

THEN WE'LL JUST LIVE THE TATTOOS, BURN, RIGHT TO THE STINKIN'...

TIK TIK

GIVE IT UP-- NOW!

MOVE, BURN!

THERE'S NO WAY OUT-- AND YOU KNOW IT!

TIK TIK TIK TIK

I KNEW LONG BEFORE I SAW HIM...

IT'S *NOT THE COPS*, CRASH!

WHAT--?

IT'S JUST ONE MAN!

IT'S *HIM*, CRASH-- *HIM*-- AND HE *DOESN'T KILL*! HE REFUSES TO KILL!

WHAT ARE YOU--

BAD IDEA TO COME *NORTH*, CRASH--*HARDLY HEAVEN*... AND HIS TURF!

I COULDN'T LOB IT TILL CRASH GOT CLEAR...

FWAK

SHUMP

...AND IT DIDN'T LOOK LIKE HE WOULD.

EVER.

CHOKT

IT WAS THE KID WHO DID IT...

GOT IT, BATMAN!

ESSSSS

...AND WHEN THERE WAS FINALLY ENOUGH ROOM...

SMOKK

...I LOBBED.

WHOOM

I FIRED UP THE SECOND ONE AS WE BARRELED BACK TOWARD THE ACID...

THROW IT, BURN! INTO THE VAT! WE AIN'T GOIN' OUT ALONE!!

FLTCH!

IF THE COPS ARE TOO SPINELESS TO TAKE US DOWN, THEN WE'LL TAKE HALF OF GOTHAM!

DON'T DO IT!

CRASH AND BURN! THROW IT -- INTO THE LOUSY VAT!!

SSSSS

I TRIED, I REALLY DID...

...BUT HE WAS FASTER.

THAP

CAPES, ROBIN!

244

WEEKS IN THE HOSPITAL, FUZZY, GRAY, AND ACHING... THEN THE HOLDING CELL, FULL OF ECHOES... ARRAIGNMENT, ALL WOOD AND BRIGHT LIGHT, A BLACK ROBE... AND FINALLY HERE, TO WRITE AND ROT.

"...TO WRITE AND ROT," HNH. MORE GARISH THAN YOUR ACCOMPLICE'S CONFESSION, BUT MATCHING IT IN EVERY IMPORTANT RESPECT.

YOU WANT TO SIGN IT NOW?

AS YOUR COURT-APPOINTED ATTORNEY, I REPEAT: YOU DO NOT HAVE TO SIGN THAT--

SHUT UP AND GO CHASE AN AMBULANCE.

FIND SOME OTHER CRASH-AND-BURN VICTIM.

AND THIS IS HOW WE KICKED BOREDOM... DIED YOUNG... STAYED PRETTY.

TWO-HUNDRED-SIXTY-NINE YEARS IN HERE...

...LIKE THIS!

HAHAHA

HA

END!

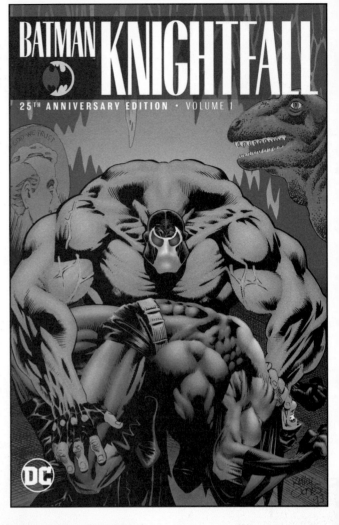

Read the classic storyline that broke the Bat!

BATMAN:
KNIGHTFALL
25th Anniversary Edition Vol. 1

BATMAN KNIGHTFALL
25th Anniversary Edition Vol. 2

BATMAN: PRELUDE TO KNIGHTFALL

READ THE ENTIRE SAGA:

BATMAN: KNIGHTQUEST:
THE CRUSADE VOL. 1

BATMAN: KNIGHTQUEST:
THE CRUSADE VOL. 2

BATMAN: KNIGHTQUEST:
THE SEARCH

BATMAN: KNIGHTSEND

BATMAN: PRODIGAL

BATMAN: TROIKA

A cataclysmic earthquake hit Gotham City.

The U.S. government deemed it uninhabitable.

Can the Dark Knight save his city?

BATMAN:
NO MAN'S LAND VOL. 1

BATMAN:
NO MAN'S LAND VOL. 2

BATMAN:
NO MAN'S LAND VOL. 3

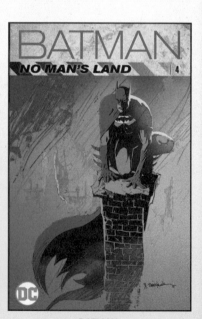

BATMAN:
NO MAN'S LAND VOL. 4